NOTHING TO SNEEZE AT

A BIOLOGIST & ALLERGY SUFFERER CRACKS
THE CODE ON ALLERGIES

CLIFF HAN

ISBN 978-1-957909-00-4

INTRODUCTION

This isn't a book about allergies. Or to be more accurate, it isn't *only* about allergies.

In the coming chapters I'm going to tell you about my childhood in China. I'll share the story of how I came to be a doctor, moved to America, and found myself working at one of the world's preeminent labs with the sharpest scientific minds. I'll even tell you a little bit about my faith, my family, and why I launched a product called *AllerPops* that (hopefully) will change the world for millions of people.

Why mix so much together into one short book? My belief is that each of us is placed into this world with a destiny and mission to fulfill. I simply found myself at the right times and places to arrive where I am today. I'm not exceptional. I'm simply open to what God, or the universe if you prefer, has ready for me.

And really, that's the point. There are many reasons you might be reading these pages, whether printed or on a tablet. Perhaps you are someone who suffers from allergies and has been searching for relief. Maybe you are an investor in my company and want to know more about me. You could even be a budding entrepreneur who wants to learn from my examples and mistakes. Regardless of what brought you here, everything aligned to bring you to my story in this moment. So, I'm going to share all of the useful parts. That way you not only take the information you need, but also put it into the proper context.

One thing I learned long ago as a practicing physician – and something that will be a running theme throughout this book – is that nothing happens independently of circumstance. Almost everything in life is dependent on situational factors. Variables like light, temperature, and contamination can wildly affect results in a lab. Likewise, the economy, competitors, and even personal relationships can all make or break a business. Where you grow up, and with whom, will affect the choices you make later in your adult years. Even the smallest coincidence can yield unexpected outcomes later.

It all matters. You can't understand the part without glancing at the whole.

Even if that weren't the case, I would want to share the salient parts of my story with you anyway. Our experiences aren't scientific papers. Without passion and meaning they are just lists of events. Certainly, rigorous academic study has its place, but a book of my collected observations on bacteria and allergy symptoms wouldn't be very interesting. Neither would it be of much help to the allergy sufferer, investor, or entrepreneur I mentioned.

So, with that piece of prologue out of the way, let me thank you for purchasing this book and taking the time to read it. By the end you will know a bit more about me. More importantly, you'll understand how I stumbled onto a new approach to allergy treatment. Hopefully you'll be as excited as I am for the potential of a safe, effective, and affordable way to deal with a problem that doesn't just affect millions of people but is becoming a bigger concern with each passing year. You will even be able to explain why allergies are more prevalent than they were in the past (which can clear up so many misunderstandings).

Before we get into all of that we need to start at the beginning. Let's look at where I come from, how I became an accidental time traveler, and why it matters to you...

If you were to ask me how I came to be on the cutting edge of allergy research, I might have to say the real answer is that it has always been my destiny to become a time traveler. I don't mean this in the traditional science fiction sense; I haven't arrived from the future to cure sneezes and watery eyes. If anything, I've come from the *past* with simple ideas that have been overlooked in the modern world.

To put it another way, I've had an unusual life, one which has provided me with unique insights into both the problem of allergies and new methods for treating them. Much of that occurred by accident when I moved from one technological era to another multiple times.

Don't worry if that doesn't make sense to you just yet. I can explain by taking you back to the beginning and walking you (briefly) through my journey from a shy and stubborn boy to genetic researcher and, eventually, inventor and entrepreneur. By the end you won't just know more about me, you'll also understand why so many of the things people have been doing to treat their allergies aren't actually making them much better.

I'll start by saying I didn't always have this sense of destiny. In fact, for most of my life I never thought about allergies at all. I was fortunate to even make my way into a career path where I could study them in the first place. After all, I wasn't born into circumstances that would have pointed towards a life in science *or* business.

ACKNOWLEDGMENTS

First, I want to thank Matt Sherwood for helping me write the book. We worked together for several months across two-years. His patience and dedication made the book project possible.

I am grateful for the participation of our early customers in using the product and giving testimonies online and in the book. Represented here are Martin, Benjamin, Karen, and Lance.

I thank my family for their support and help. Brian Han, my son, is my primary motivation to take on the journey and the book's first reader. His comments and edits improved the manuscript. Kathy Leng, my wife, has been working two jobs in the last several years to support the family as I "ran away" from that responsibility. Shena Han, my daughter, helped the project with her witty thinking and critical comments.

Thanks to Paul Scott and his team for designing the cover I like so much. I thank Sonja Dewing, my publisher, for her magic touches on the book and for charting the path to have the book to be printed, listed, and promoted.

Lastly, I thank my Lord for giving me a purpose in this life that made it possible to complete the project.

1

MY LIFE AS A TIME TRAVELER

Everyone Starts Somewhere

My parents raised me in a small village called Hanlou. It was, and is, a rural area located in the Shan Dong province of China, several hours south of Beijing. You may have noticed that my last name, Han, is very similar to the name of my hometown. That's no coincidence. Of the five hundred or so people who lived there, all but a small handful were also Hans. We shared a common ancestor, on my father's side, who founded the village about three hundred years ago.

My family made do with limited food, clothes, or covered spaces. We had fifteen Hans, covering three generations, living in a single hut with no running water. Our toilet was an outdoor pit, and the yard was filled with pigs and chickens. Instead of diapers, the toddlers wore pants that opened at the bottom and were cleaned from a bucket. It was a normal upbringing for that time and place.

My mother was a tough, hardworking woman. She was born in the 1930s, an era when parents would bind the feet of young girls to make them smaller and supposedly more feminine. As a result, she suffered deformities that made it difficult for her to walk without pain. And yet, she not only managed to stay on top of our home, but also contributed financially by doing work for our village.

Although most people worked around the village, my father spent most of his weeks away from home. So did his three brothers. That was because they had the rarest of advantages: *an education.*

My grandfather had wanted his children to learn. My oldest uncle received private tutoring. My next uncle went to public school. My father, the third boy, was given a middle school education. All three were able to get more prestigious and better-paying jobs (like a teacher or government administrator) as a result. That made us luckier than most, but it also meant my father could be away for weeks or months at a time.

Whether in the town nearby or farther from home, all the sons of my grandpa had jobs. That left the women to tend to the communal village farm. All the land belonged to the community and each family was assigned a team that would tend to a specific area or task. The harvest would be divided according to the success of the crop, the size of a family, and the amount of work each had performed.

Additionally, villagers could earn extra money by finding employment in factories or working for the government. My mother chose to work at one of these jobs. Roads were being paved in the nearby city of Tengzhou and villagers could help by hauling stones to a new gravel-making facility that had sprung up in the area. My mom (along with her sister-in-law) would venture up a small hill, two or three miles from the factory, and bring the rocks back by cart. It would have been backbreaking work for anyone, and particularly a woman who couldn't walk without pain.

One thing I will always remember about my mother was the way she could be so quiet you might almost forget she was in a room. I took after this trait, to the point that I once over-heard one of my classmates telling a family member that something must have been wrong with me because they thought I couldn't speak at a normal volume. I just happened to be very quiet and shy. In fact, it took me many years to conquer that part of my personality and become more outgoing.

My father wasn't loud by any means either, but luckily he was more outgoing than myself or my mother. Despite having only been to school through the seventh grade, he became a teacher and administrator. Those were relatively good jobs for the time and place.

As I mentioned, he would often leave home for weeks and months at a time. That was because he could be assigned to a school or office 40 or 50 miles away. In those days people tended to walk from one place to another, or occasionally hitch rides on tractors. Bikes were a luxury and cars were virtually unseen. So, being posted a few villages away felt like the equivalent of working in another state or province.

Today, we might talk of someone who grew up with poverty and an absent parent as having a tough childhood, but it certainly didn't feel that way to me. Along with my older sister and younger brother, I had the freedom to run and play in the village. I had my mother to look after me, along with aunts, uncles, grandparents, and even neighbors. We may not have had money or luxuries, but we didn't have much to worry about, either.

Besides, we were luckier than most. My family was well respected. We were looked up to as those living on the more prosperous west side of the village where officials lived. Even my father's absences, as difficult as they were to endure, reminded me of how fortunate we were. Most people from our area never traveled farther away than the next village on the road. To be important enough to be needed elsewhere was a sign of prestige.

Looking back, I also think it's possible that seeing my father and uncles come and go planted the seed of travel and adventure into my soul. Although I would miss them, their departures would make me think about the larger world beyond Hanlou. Where were they going? And when would it be my turn to see something new and different?

My First Brush With Allergies

My days were spent running barefoot with my friends through streets and fields. As you might imagine, that sort of lifestyle led to lots of minor scrapes and bruises. Occasionally these would be serious enough that I would be taken to our village doctor. His preferred method of treatment was to administer what we called Mercury Red, which was short for the simple antiseptic mercurochrome, onto wounds. It got its nickname from the dark smears it left on the skin.

Because of my adventurous nature I was treated with Mercury Red fairly frequently. Over time, my parents noticed the applications left my skin irritated and blotchy, as if I had developed eczema. They raised this concern with the doctor, who studied one of the affected areas and announced that I had an allergy to the medication. This didn't mean much to me as an eight-year-old, of course, but it was my first lesson that your body could fight something that was supposed to be good for you.

Having a slight allergy to medicine was a fairly minor complaint. China was on the cusp of a great transition. Technology and modern conveniences hadn't reached us yet. Many families went without enough food. All the other kids in my school were very thin. You could usually see their ribs sticking through skin if they went shirtless. Some had misshapen bodies or disfigured legs, the side effects of malnutrition. Nearly everyone was infested with worms and parasites of one kind or another. In fact, they were so pervasive that teachers gave all of us the same medicines to get rid of them. There was no need to test before administering them because it was just assumed that we were all affected.

Most kids and adults weren't that worried about keeping clean. Although we bathed outside from time to time, we weren't afraid of a little dirt. I can remember one occasion when my grandfather decided that my first uncle, who already had six kids of his own, should have a new house. Most of the men had been working away from home, but all the sons and fathers from the area returned to the village to help with the construction. As kids, our job was to make mud that could be used as an adhesive.

This was a wonderful job. First, we would spread a layer of dirt. Then we would add some wheat stalk that had been cut short for the mixture, and finally add more dirt and water. There was nothing quite so dirty – and exhilarating – as having an adult throw a bucket of water into the dirt so we could roll around and slap piles of sludge together. No one thought twice about things like that. Weren't kids supposed to be playing in mud and puddles?

It probably won't surprise you to know that we weren't exposed to any sort of oral hygiene, either. I was in middle school before I ever saw my first toothbrush and didn't learn about flossing until I reached college. Again, this wasn't at all unusual. No one in my village worried about things like that.

I can still remember being in sixth grade, the first year of middle school, when a teacher asked us to stick some work we had completed on the back wall of the classroom. We didn't have commercially produced glue available, so I would normally bring a bit of leftover porridge from home. However, on that day I had forgotten to. As I stood next to my paper, wondering what I would do, a friend noticed my dilemma. He told me not to worry: "You have glue with you." With that he opened his mouth, scratched his fingernail across his teeth, and put the slimy, sticky biofilm on his own paper and hung it on the wall. I did the same.

These sorts of stories seem strange in the modern world I live in now, but in that context they just represented the facts of life. In that respect my early childhood represented a first stop on my time-traveling journey. Technologically speaking, the world that existed in 1960s and early 1970s rural China was probably 200 years behind the life I enjoy today in New Mexico. Of course, you don't realize you're living in the past when it's the only life you've ever known, so it didn't trouble me.

Looking back, life probably *was* difficult. Still, I actually feel incredibly grateful for those experiences I had as a child. We felt wild and free, which is less common for today's youth. Besides, there were some longer-term benefits, as well. For one thing, that era of my life has given me an acute appreciation for all that I enjoy such a relatively short time later. And for another, my childhood gave me a different perspective on hygiene and medicine that wasn't available to some of my colleagues.

Moving an Era Ahead

The school system that existed in rural China at the time wasn't nearly as structured as what you might expect to see today. I didn't start attending classes until sometime after my seventh birthday. In fact, I can remember a neighbor shouting at me in the street and asking, "Why aren't you in school?" one day when I was playing on a pile of dirt in the streets. Whether this was cause or coincidence I don't know, but I found myself in a classroom not long after.

I was generally an above-average student without being exceptional. My father never pushed me directly to succeed in academics. Instead, he would tell his friends and neighbors about how I liked to study, making sure I was in earshot when he did. I wasn't bothered by these subtle reminders. I had a very curious mind. I always wanted to know more about the way the world worked. At the same time, though, I had picked up a stubborn streak from my mother. My inability to let things go, or just follow along, probably hindered my grades.

There were many different times when my "persistent nature" got me into trouble. On one occasion a teacher informed my father that I hadn't been doing my homework properly. I don't remember the details, except to say I felt much differently about what I had turned in. It seemed to me that I had done exactly what I should have. Both my father and the instructor asked me to change my work so I could get a better grade. I refused – not because I couldn't do the assignment or was worried about the effort, but because I was sure in my heart that I was correct.

On other occasions I challenged different teachers at my school. For instance, once my class was given a test. I had finished and was chatting with the boy next to me when our instructor said: "Do not steal other people's answers." I wondered who the teacher was talking to. He pointed at me. I insisted that I hadn't cheated, but he accused me again. I got so angry that I tore my test in half. He made me leave the classroom and eventually I had to retake the exam.

I also argued with my brother once in a while. It didn't happen often, but one day I got angry and threw rocks at him when he hid from me on the roof of the house. I wasn't a troublemaker, but I couldn't have been easy to raise, either.

Whether it was because my parents wanted me to get a

better education or were just worried I would find myself in worse trouble I can't say, but eventually I was sent to live with my father in a nearby town for my second year of middle school. That move didn't just provide me with a fresh start and new teachers. It also moved me ahead to another era in time.

My father's apartment wasn't lavish by any means, but it had luxuries I had never seen before. We traveled on paved roads to reach the apartment, and when we arrived there were fresh wonders like running water and electricity. It was amazing! You could pull a string and have a light come on in any room of the house, and at any time of the day or night.

By coincidence it was around that time when we started learning about the magic of electricity in a physics class. During a break in our studies I noticed a pair of naked wires in a room where students could play table tennis. My mind started to wonder about the connection between what I saw in front of me and what we had learned from our instructor. Were the wires hot, I wondered? Did they connect to anything? And what would happen if I put them together?

Like any good science student I decided to get answers. I wandered over and slowly, methodically, moved the two wires next to one another. When they finally met I was rewarded by a spark, followed by complete darkness.

While the other students began asking each other whether we were having a power outage I realized I had made a mistake. Most circuits didn't have fuses then, and I had caused a short. That could lead to a fire. I had to separate the wires I had brought together, and quickly. I swung my hands around in the darkness, grasping for the places where my mind imagined them. Finally I managed to pull them apart. The lights came back on and the games continued. It was one of the first times I realized how theory and research could be put to work in the real world.

. . .

SCANNING the Horizon

SCHOOLS IN CHINA weren't that organized at the time, and educational standards weren't high. I have already mentioned my father was qualified to teach elementary school even though he had only made it to the second year of middle school himself. Most of my elementary instructors had made it only a year or two farther than he had.

While my generation had more access to education, the guidelines were changing all the time. After five years of primary school and three years of middle school, I was eligible to apply for a two-year high school program. Some students skipped this step and went straight to work. I decided to keep going with more classes.

I was fortunate to have that option. The local schools were just transitioning from a two-year middle school program to a three-year curriculum. I hadn't passed my exam on the first try, following my second year, but was successful after the extra year.

It seemed as if a second stroke of luck had arrived when the high school I was signed up to attend was in the same town where I had been living with my father. However, just as I was set to begin he was transferred to a new job. It was in the same city, but eight miles away – too far to walk or bike daily.

My father reached out to his connections and was able to find a room for me in a dormitory for local officials where he had once lived. I would have preferred to be home with my family, but my accommodations were nicer than the ones many of my classmates enjoyed. I had my own bed, for instance, whereas many other students in the high school dormitory slept on a shared six feet by forty feet wood board, supported 3 feet above ground. with each person occupying an area about three feet wide. Things weren't perfect, but I was grateful.

This was a transitional period in my life. While I enjoyed my studies, it was difficult for me to connect with many of my fellow students. Not only was I shy and short on confidence, but I lived away from them in a separate place. There weren't many ways for me to connect or integrate myself into the group. I had a small talent for ping-pong, and liked to play after class, but didn't really fit into the established teams and social circles that had gradually sorted themselves out. I wasn't right for most clubs or cliques, so I was largely left to do my own thing.

There was a regular highlight to my days, however. The dormitory where I lived housed one student and significantly more government administrators. These were important people, and so the building was supplied with running water.

That water came from a tower that stood three stories high. It was located just behind the kitchen, a brick cylinder with a concrete tank at the top. The whole thing was maintained by the cooks who worked in the building. They needed to start and stop a pump sometimes, depending on whether the water tank was full or empty. You could tell by an indicator arrow that was visible from the outside.

Quite often the arrow would be blown off its track and entangle itself in the nearby ladder. When this happened the cooks would ask me to go up the ladder and fix it so they could continue on with their own duties. At first, I would solve the issue and come straight back down. Over time, though, I gained the freedom and courage to climb to spend time at the top enjoying the view.

While it might have fallen under the category of a "chore," I loved climbing that metal ladder every day. Each step brought me closer to the highest point in my town – and indeed for several miles in any direction. At that sort of height you couldn't just see farther than anyone else, you could scan the horizon and get a sense of what was happening all throughout the region. I could see my school with its running track and the fields beyond. My eyes could follow the narrow roads leading out of town, with aspen and elm trees dotting the way. Farther afield were acres and acres of corn and soybeans, adding color and freshness to the sights.

What was even more amazing than what I could see, however, was what I *couldn't*. With time I learned to take in the view and let the perspective fuel my imagination. I started to imagine what might be past those fields and in other parts of my province or the world at large.

It was a small thing, but that small responsibility probably helped me in ways that I never really appreciated. That's because the world around me was falling into change and turmoil. A mindset of curiosity, and inability to think about unknown challenges, would be exactly what was required to make it through the next phase of my life.

2

UNPLANNED ADVENTURES

No matter where you live, or what culture you're from, your teenage years are always a transformative time. In my case, the normal growth and awkwardness were mirrored by the fact that my entire country was growing up along with me.

It all started when Chairman Mao died in 1976. That set off a series of reforms in China's culture and economy at every level. What was particularly pertinent to me was the fact that in 1977 the government created a national test for those who wanted to attend college. Not only were more spots opened up for higher learning, but the system would now be based on academic merit rather than being solely about family connections and affiliations.

That was good news for many, but there was a catch: the test would be open to *everyone*. Because they hadn't had the chance to be educated in the past, many people in their twenties and thirties wanted to take the exams along with students who were graduating from high school during my years. It was a free-for-all academic competition.

It was impossible to know what my odds of making it into

any Chinese college would be under those circumstances. I certainly wasn't top of my class, and only had two years of high school to draw from. Still, I thought taking more classes, and hopefully finding a career path I would be interested in, would be preferable to signing up for a life of physical labor. So, I decided to enroll for the exam and take my chances.

It wasn't a decision I took lightly. Along with the stress of taking a test that could determine the course of your future, there were more immediate discomforts. Because the testing location was situated across the city, I had to make a long bike journey while carrying a blanket and mosquito net on my back. You needed to arrive the day before the exam was adminis- tered, so I got a taste of the communal living and harsh sleeping conditions my classmates had been through. It wasn't the sort of environment that made it easy to feel relaxed and prepared.

The test itself was nerve-racking. I knew there was nothing left to do except try my best and put what I'd learned in high school to work. At the end of the exam you filled in a form to indicate your choice of schools at each of the four possible ranks – a four-year program at a national university, a second- rank four-year college, a three-year junior college, or a two-year vocational school.

My dream at the time was to study geology and mining. As a teenager I'd found myself immersed in a series of novels about scientists who studied the earth and its metals. I wanted to be like them. I didn't have strong preferences beyond that, but there were only two choices for junior colleges: teaching and medicine. I knew I was much too shy and quiet to ever speak in front of a classroom, so I chose the medical program in junior college as my fallback selection.

It was difficult to assess my own performance. And of course I couldn't expect the results to arrive quickly; there were weeks of waiting for the scores to be displayed on a wall of the school. When they finally came, the verdict was mixed – I had qualified for higher education, but only at the junior college level. I had been assigned to three years of medical school at Jining Medical College. Being accepted was an "in or out" option. I had to either accept or move on.

I talked with my family about declining the offer. Although choices were limited, I did have the possibility of sitting through another year of high school and taking the test again. That seemed like the best way forward to me, but my father advised me to take the opportunity I was given. After all, with competition for the exams growing year after year, how sure could I be that I would even qualify at all the next time around?

In the end I came around to his point of view. Like so many other things in life it turned out to be a decision that would seem to work out poorly in the short term only to pay bigger dividends later.

My First Attempt at Higher Education

BECAUSE I HAVE high school-aged children, I know that American students plan for many years to get into medical school. They work long hours, take numerous tests, and even sign up for after-school activities so they can improve their applications and increase the odds they will be accepted to a program that will turn them into a doctor.

My journey wasn't like that at all. Although I knew I was fortunate to qualify for more education, I wasn't thrilled to be placed into a three-year community college-level medical program.

What all of this meant for me was that committing to that school and putting myself on a career path that I wasn't excited about... at least for a while. What I figured out later was that there is always a way forward for someone who is either stubborn or persistent enough, depending on your point of view.

In any case, my community college education was in many ways an extension of high school. I studied a lot and mostly kept to myself. In fact, my social life was nearly non-existent. I occasionally spoke to the six other students who slept in the same dorm as I did, but rarely used my voice outside of those confines.

My shy nature made it difficult to make friends, and nearly impossible for me to date. There were 50 students that were admitted to my program. Five of them were women. To the best of my memory, I didn't speak to any of them, even once, for the first two years.

Keeping quiet brought academic challenges, as well. During the third year of our program we were required to rotate through different departments in a hospital. Even simple verbal tasks, like offering updates on a patient's condition for the day, were challenging for me.

Luckily, I was doing better with the parts of the program that didn't require me to speak. Classes were all about the basics of anatomy, diagnosis, first aid, and medication. I enjoyed the learning aspect of my coursework. The textbooks and lectures taught me about skeletons, muscles, nerves, and organs. There was a great deal to figure out and understand. The mental challenge made it easy for me to study the material late into the night, reading and rereading sections several times over. I did well on my exams and progressed through the program without too much difficulty.

Still, I wasn't very enthusiastic about my career path. I figured it wouldn't be too long before I was administering Mercury Red to a new generation of students. My life seemed as if it were on a very predictable trajectory. However, there were two noteworthy things that happened in those few years.

The first seemed completely inconsequential at the time. As I have already mentioned, hygiene and personal cleansing weren't really emphasized when I was growing up. They weren't addressed very heavily in my medical program, either, but as budding doctors we were introduced to ideas about oral care and flossing. I didn't pay a great deal of attention, but it was around this time I learned that your mouth had all kinds of bacteria that could (and supposedly should) be removed. That helped explain why my "glue" had gone away when I started brushing my teeth in middle school.

Everything I learned as a medical student was focused on using tools and chemicals to "clean" yourself. This was the first time I was exposed to flossing, for instance, although it was many more years before I began to practice the habit.

The other, more immediately significant shift was that I was required to take a course in genetics. I found myself fascinated by the subject, its applications, and especially the research methods that were involved. Even to this day I am enthralled by Mendel's classic study of the garden pea. The idea that you could know about something that was invisible by looking at the observable parts of an elegant design delighted me. I admired the beauty and grace of the research, and still find myself inspired by it.

I also found genetics to be fascinating from the standpoint of its often unseen impact on our lives. By understanding things like genomes and markers you could literally predict someone's future health. That seemed far more exciting to me than treating bloody scrapes and broken limbs. I decided then and there that I would eventually make my way into that field of study. I didn't know how I would do it, but it became my mission.

As you might have guessed, that wasn't going to be an easy transition to make.

. . .

A Fresh Mental Challenge

If my medical school assignment had been a bit of a disappointment, then my first career posting wasn't much better. Following my graduation from the three-year program I was assigned to work in a psychiatric facility roughly five miles from my family's home.

To be fair, this was actually an upgrade over some of the possibilities that had been in front of me. There was the very real chance that I would be sent to work as a village doctor, much like the one I had known, in some far-away town. At least my first job would allow me to stay in contact with my family while giving me a glimpse of advancement in the future. It wasn't what I had wanted or hoped for, but I tried to see the benefits and advantages that were in front of me.

Given that most of you probably didn't grow up in 1980s China the way I did, this might be a good time to point out that I had very few choices to work with. It wasn't as if I could simply choose another place to work. Because the state administered your education, gave you exams, and paid your educational costs, it was entirely up to them to decide what you were suited to learn and where you would apply those lessons. Perhaps, if you were lucky enough to have wealth or family connections, you *might* be able to make a "gift" that would open up your options or steer you in another direction. I was lucky that my father had a series of government jobs, but not lucky enough to exercise that sort of influence.

Still, I couldn't deny that this was the kind of job no one wanted. Psychiatry was not given much respect at the time, and the hospital was a difficult place to work. The general perception was that it was filled with "crazy people," and that the doctors who worked there were looked down upon by other medical professionals.

The facility itself was an old church that had been

constructed in the early twentieth century. There were brick walls and wooden floors. The government had taken the building over in 1949, originally for the purpose of treating soldiers who had come back from combat with mental sickness. Gradually, a broader range of patients were admitted. By the time I arrived it was filled with those who were suffering from ailments like bipolar disorder or schizophrenia.

Some of those patients could be treated. Most had no chance of being cured. The facilities were locked up twenty-four hours a day, seven days a week. For doctors, duties mostly included prescribing medications that would make patients sleepy. Occasionally you might increase or decrease a dosage, or administer electric shocks, but everything was geared towards mitigating symptoms as no permanent solutions were available. In the very best instances patients would be able to leave for a few months, or perhaps a year. But almost all of them ended up coming back to us sooner or later.

It goes without saying that the patients weren't excited about being housed in our facility. Neither were most of the staff. Despite the fact that we had few options and little control over our future, a majority of the doctors and nurses I worked with were desperate to escape. They took jobs in distant places, or even accepted demotions, just to get away from the sense of never-ending dread that was so persistent in that building. As for myself, I still dreamed of finding a way to move into genetic research.

To make that happen I'd have to go back to the classroom. In order to prepare myself for bigger possibilities, such as the graduate school admittance exam, I intensified my study of the English language. English was the most difficult portion in the exam and could not be prepared for in a short amount of time. I had taken two years of classes in high school before restarting with the basics again in college. Now, as a working professional, it seemed like time to learn my ABCs one more time.

Improving my English was a steep hill to climb. Despite having been top of my class in the subject in high school, I couldn't say much. I knew enough words to get through simple books and publications, though, so while working at the hospital I started reading *China Daily*. That was the only English language newspaper available. I went through it each day trying to master basic words and sentence structures.

I'm not sure if I just wanted to pass an exam or thought that studying a foreign language might eventually lead to a new opportunity somewhere farther away. Maybe it was a bit of both. Either way, I started to achieve a kind of basic fluency with English language reading and writing that would pay off later in life.

One other nice thing about working in the hospital was that it afforded me a chance to spend more time with my family again. In the handful of years that had passed since I had left home, the technology for manufacturing and maintaining bicycles in China had improved significantly. They had become affordable enough that I could have one and pedal the five miles from their house in the city to my work each morning and then go home at night. Occasionally it would be dark or cold enough that I would have to spend the night at the hospital, as many staff members did, but I tried my best to get away whenever it was possible.

It was through my family that seasonal allergies entered my mind again. You might assume they would have come up in my medical program, but they were barely mentioned. There simply weren't enough patients with allergies in China to worry about teaching treatments for them. Nor did I know many people who suffered from allergies in my personal life. This lack of knowledge came back to bite me as a fresh graduate in the working world.

I was a newly minted medical professional with a three-year degree. I might have been working in a psychiatric hospital, but I had vastly more education than the rest of my family. It was only reasonable, then, that my father called one day with a medical question. I was proud and eager to show off all I had learned. When it came to the body, I felt like I knew *everything*. In the coming years I learned, as all medical professionals do, that we collectively understand very little. But at the time I felt prepared to take on whatever issue or ailment he would describe.

Confident and concentrating, I listened as my father described the problems a good friend was having with his health. What could be done, my father wondered, about sneezing, watery eyes, and other symptoms stemming from exposure to pollen? I had to admit that I didn't really know. In the end I advised common antihistamines and told his friend to avoid pollen – in other words, what any retail pharmacy worker would have told him. I think both myself and my father were slightly embarrassed that I couldn't give a better answer.

After that conversation, allergies once again receded from my mind. Life went by. I didn't have any hint that my destiny was calling to me. On the contrary, most of my energy was devoted to plotting a path that led away from the psychiatric hospital, and possibly medicine altogether. I needed to find a way into a higher-level university.

Changing Course

IF GETTING into a college program had been difficult, then being admitted to graduate school was going to be even tougher. In fact, I knew that less than twenty percent of applicants were accepted. So, I simply took my time and let my persistent nature take over. I looked through textbooks and guides in my spare hours, working on areas of my knowledge that I felt could use an improvement. Finally in 1989, after four years of work at the psychiatric hospital, I was ready to take my chance.

It required years of intense study but my application to an advanced program in Suzhou Medical College, currently part of Soochow University, was a success. My advisor was Dr. Caiyun Wu, who led the psychiatric department in the hospital affiliated with the medical college. Naturally, I didn't have much choice over my field of study. Because I had been assigned to a psychiatric hospital, my master's degree would have to be in psychiatry. After all, the assumption was that I would take what I would learn and help further the state by going back to my old role (or something close to it) with improved knowledge.

There wasn't a good way to get around these restrictions. I had to get permission from the hospital to apply to graduate school at all. And even after I was accepted they could control my destiny. That's because each person had written employment records that were needed to secure a new job. If your previous employer wouldn't release them, then you couldn't move on. In that way my administrators had a great deal of power over my work and destiny. And even if all those limitations hadn't been in place, it was still true that psychiatry was the only field where I had any real experience.

Still, my years of college and work had made me a bit wiser

than I had been as a teenager. I would need to enroll in the program they had approved, but I didn't necessarily need to follow their plan. I arrived with an alternate path in mind.

I did indeed study psychiatry, just as I was assigned. However, when it came time to complete the research project needed to graduate, I joined a study that investigated the cellular genetics of Alzheimer's disease. In that way I was able to fulfill my obligation *and* steer towards my passions for data and DNA. Instead of working in the psychiatry clinic, I spent most of the last two years of research time in a cytogenetics lab led by Professor Jingsheng Gao, who co-advised my thesis study. Through that research I became familiar with the chromosomal aspects of dementia and related diseases. I was able to combine my previous experience with my real interests.

Meanwhile, as I was busy learning in classrooms and labs, China kept changing around me. The opening economy created new opportunities in business. People who might have been interested in joining academia or looking for government work were suddenly interested in capitalist enterprises. They realized there were ways to make a good living that didn't involve several years of work, study, and political strategizing just to get started.

While it had been difficult to get into college, and even harder to make it to graduate school, the economic and societal changes taking place had virtually emptied out doctoral programs. There simply wasn't enough money in advanced education to attract new students. Applications were decreasing for all kinds of programs, meaning that I could continue my education if I wanted to.

As I neared graduation from my master's program, I learned that only two of the members of our class, myself and one other, were interested in going even further. I talked with my academic advisors, each of whom encouraged me to take the next step. The odds were in my favor. And even better, I could finally pursue my passions.

Moving On

The only logical way forward for me was to pursue a PhD. Even though much of my competition had disappeared, there were still hurdles that needed to be overcome. I first needed to pass the school's entry test. This turned out to be trickier than it initially seemed.

As with my first graduate school application, I had to complete a portion of the exam designed to test on the knowledge of the English language. This wasn't just the hardest part of the test, but also the most confusing. I could do translations back and forth, but it wasn't clear whether the answers for other parts of the exam were meant to be given in Chinese. When I asked for clarification I found the test inspector wasn't able to give me clear advice either way. The test was simply too new. I decided to follow my instincts and use my native language since it would allow me to express myself more precisely on the non-English portions of the exam.

Weeks later I was notified I had failed, and with a score that was unbelievably low. Being the stubborn person I am, I decided to make inquiries and found that the misunderstanding had indeed caused me to miss points. I explained the issue as best I could to administrators and, in a surprising moment of flexibility, they decided to reverse their decision. They also changed the wording on the exam to make things clearer to future applicants.

With that obstacle cleared, all that remained was an interview hosted by C.C. Tan, a pioneer of modern Chinese genetics. Meeting him was a delight and, although I was nervous, I was granted admission.

In 1992 I enrolled at Fudan University and joined my country's premier molecular genetics doctoral program. Looking back, I was incredibly fortunate. Not only was I able to reverse a failing test score because of a minor communication issue, but I also happened to apply at the right time in China's history.

I've already mentioned that many students were looking to business, rather than higher education, during that window of opportunity. As chance would have it, there were only two applicants that year. We both got in. It might have been impossible to have secured a spot just a couple of years before. Likewise, the system of supply and demand corrected itself shortly thereafter, to the point that it might have been impossible for me to enroll in the same program just a couple of years after I did. Luck guided me into the perfect window of time to apply. The hand of fate was starting to nudge me a little more firmly.

The work I did at that university was intense but enjoyable. I had a deep interest in genetics, but not much foundational knowledge in the area. That meant I had to catch up on topics that most other incoming students would already be fluent in, all while taking on new material. On top of that, I sat in on undergraduate classes related to computer science. It would have been impossible to design the studies we needed without taking advantage of data management tools. However, computers were relatively new to me, so I spent a lot of time learning how to program and manage different tables, formulas, and desktop interfaces.

Determined as I was to learn, it would have been impossible to catch up without the assistance of my instructors. Professor Shouyuan Zhao became my PhD advisor, helping shape my study and research. Additionally, Professor Long Yu served as my co-advisor. He had just finished his postdoctoral work and joined the faculty. He was roughly ten years my senior and agreed to take me on as his first PhD student.

While most of my learning occurred in the classroom, this was a time when I began to grow in other ways, as well. For instance, during a visit to one of the rural villages near my university I noticed something interesting. There were popular T-shirts being sold for less in the city than they were in the outlying areas. I speculated the difference came to much more than you would expect when you factored in commercial transport costs. I realized the rural markup was substantial enough that a budding entrepreneur *just might* be able to make a profit by purchasing them close to home and transporting them to markets farther away.

The whole venture seemed simple enough, and it gave me some early exposure to the idea of starting a business. I didn't make much money, though, and couldn't really justify the time that was required as my studies became more intense. After an attempt at buying and reselling the shirts back in my hometown during a summer vacation, I gave the idea up. I could be incredibly persistent about some things, but discovered I didn't care enough about shirts to make the project work. Besides, I had too many other demands on my time. Even so, I got my first small taste of entrepreneurial life.

As time went on my studies intensified. When I wasn't in a classroom or library, I was in the lab with my advisor. He and I had built everything we needed to study genetics in that room from the ground up. We even designed and installed the shelves and tables in our lab. There were days when we would work from seven in the morning until ten or eleven at night with very few breaks. Once in a while we might take off a holiday, or enjoy a small break on Sunday. For the most part, though, we threw ourselves into the effort.

Make no mistake: it definitely was *work*. Outsiders may think of scientific endeavors as being scholarly or relaxed, but our environment felt closer to a factory floor than a library. Our research revolved around generating a detailed map of artificial yeast chromosomes. Just getting the basics together and verifying what a researcher from another institute had already completed took several months of tedious and repetitive effort.

Even the long hours and seemingly menial tasks brought lessons, however. Whenever a process had to be repeated again and again, I would find myself searching for ways to increase the speed or accuracy. Over hundreds of repetitions I learned to refine my thinking and be more intentional with my movements. Each new change and improvement brought me a small bit of satisfaction and helped pass the time.

It took three and a half years to make it through and earn my PhD. I can honestly say it was one of the hardest things I've ever done, and that the mental intensity nearly broke me. What I learned, though – besides the genome structure of a human – is that most of us have a much deeper reserve of energy and fight than we could ever possibly realize. When we find something that matters enough to us we can always go that little extra bit further.

While I was mainly focused on genetics and computers, I continued my education in other areas, as well. In fact, as my doctoral work progressed I got deeper into my study of the English language. My interest was no longer a relaxing hobby. Much of the emerging research in the field of genetics was coming from Western schools and laboratories. Whereas Russian had been the extra language of choice just a few years before, more and more students were now picking up English. I was fortunate to have gotten a head start.

It was during these years that the idea of moving away crept into my mind more frequently. Part of me loved the idea of an overseas adventure, not to mention the chance to work with bigger teams and better equipment than we had in China. Maybe I had simply outgrown my local water towers and needed to take a wider view of the world. Either way, I found myself keeping my eyes open for opportunities beyond China's borders.

These thoughts came into closer focus as I approached my graduation. With a PhD in molecular genetics I was finally free of the kind of career path that would land me in a village hospital or psychiatric ward (as a doctor *or* a patient). I could have stayed within the Chinese health system, of course, or even continued working at the university. However, I also knew big things were happening around the globe.

In 1995 I met a visiting scholar by the name of Bob Moyzis, who headed up the Center for Human Genome Studies at Los Alamos National Laboratory with the US Department of Energy. At that time, the Human Genome Project was in its early stages. He presented a sample of his work at our school and I was able to attend. After hearing him speak about the work, I knew I wanted to be involved.

Colleagues and advisors on both sides of the Pacific warned me that there would be extensive background checks, security screenings, and other paperwork hassles involved in a move to the US. Luckily, my stubborn nature wouldn't let me give up on the idea. So, after dozens of letters, applications, and interviews I was offered a position in Los Alamos, New Mexico. The next stop was getting approval for a Chinese passport to travel abroad, a process that wasn't necessarily going to be easy or successful. Eventually, though, I was informed of my approval from our local police. It had taken more than six months of follow-up and waiting to get permission from both sides of the Pacific Ocean, but I was going to be one of the lucky ones.

As excited as I was to finally begin the kind of career I had always hoped for, that was a difficult time in my life. Besides the normal worries that come to anyone who is moving to a new country and culture, I struggled to say goodbye to my family. My parents and siblings were happy for me, but there was also a degree of sadness involved. My father, in particular, always thought I would get a taste of life in different cities and places and then return home. I felt sorry that I couldn't make his wish come true.

Still, my loved ones did everything they could to put on a brave face and send me off into the world with their support. They gathered money, mementos, and even a thick quilt for my journey to America. Things were about to change dramatically again.

3

NEW HORIZONS

In my high school days I used to sit at the top of our town's water tower and scan the horizon to figure out what was waiting beyond the streets and places I knew. I always wanted to look a little farther, and to see a little more. But now, just a decade later, life had nudged me in an entirely new direction. Suddenly I was confronted with the kinds of changes I could never have expected or planned for.

As exciting as it was to move to the United States, I was overwhelmed by the differences all around me. *Everything* looked and sounded different in America. The food was new, the people seemed alien to me, and even the landscape had a different personality. I enjoyed the adventure of being in Los Alamos, but I can't say the transition was easy.

Although it was and is well-known as a hub for science and government agencies, Los Alamos in 1996 didn't even look like an organized settlement to me. There was dry, wild vegetation everywhere. The park in the middle of the town featured a pond with little water. Everything looked so empty.

It was a far cry from the hustle and bustle of my university setting in China, but there were lots of things to love. For instance, you could get peace and quiet at any time of day or night. In fact, the evenings gave me a chance to see more stars than I'd ever imagined.

In addition, I found my work to be very fulfilling. Being brought into the Human Genome Project was a blessing. Although there was a great deal to do every day, I was exposed to different backgrounds, tools, and technology. The West was certainly more prosperous, and that meant more resources for curious minds like those of us at the Department of Energy.

I had worried that I might struggle to keep up with the other scientists. In reality, my work ethic kept me productive in the lab; it was the culture and language barriers that were harder to overcome. Not only was I painfully shy, but my spoken English skills weren't very strong. I said little more than "hi" in conversations with my colleagues, and offered less than that in meetings or presentations.

With the help of my new friends and coworkers, I was gradually able to settle in. First, they helped me find a car and learn to drive. Then, someone went with me to buy a television so I could listen to English language programs in my spare time. Culture shock and my own introversion made this a slow process, but I began to adapt.

I knew that my life would be changing when I left China, but I was only beginning to sense just how thoroughly the decisions I'd made would put me on an entirely new course. This period in my life also marks the point where my story starts to be about you. It was far from obvious to me then, but my destiny was beginning to come into focus at the edges.

Becoming an American Family Man

I could write entire volumes about my work with the Human Genome Project, but those pages probably wouldn't be of great interest to someone who wants to know about allergy treatments or my growing business. So, I'll simply point out that there was a great deal of molecular biology work to be done. Most of my days were spent in a radiation laboratory where our goal was to map and sequence the human chromosome 16.

Imagine a road map, with its printed streets, intersections, and landmarks. A map of the human genome has markers, too, in the form of DNA. In fact, there are thousands of them on chromosome 16, and they can be used to isolate larger sections – usually hundreds of kilobytes long – and align them sequentially. The next step is to break them into smaller pieces and read the genetic information encoded within. As you can probably imagine, it was a slow and methodical process that took many years.

To an outsider, what we were doing might have seemed boring and difficult. And I suppose in some ways it was. However, everyone in that lab knew we were on the forefront of new breakthroughs and understanding. Without that knowledge it would have been a chore. But, with the understanding that we were improving human life, it became a mission.

I feel like that lesson was worth even more to me than the scientific knowledge we gained. *Purpose gives you power and energy.*

While work might have been tough and fulfilling, my personal life was also undergoing something of a transition. At first I was simply adjusting to my new country. Then, I got into a comfortable routine of understanding the language, along with local customs like driving, banking, and so on. My social circles grew ever so slightly and I began to feel at home in New Mexico.

However, I understood that something was missing. I wanted to start a family.

Dating had always represented an enormous challenge for me. I had had relationships with women in my school days, but shyness and self-doubt made it difficult for me to meet new partners. I suspected that my family members, who had given up on asking about my romantic prospects, had assumed I wouldn't meet anyone. They might have been right if the internet hadn't come along. But, with billions of people online, it made it easier to find someone who could see past my quiet and reserved nature.

This was the late '90s. Online dating wasn't quite the huge industry and spectacle it is today. Still, it was possible to go on the internet and connect with other people who might share your same interests. That medium was especially valuable to me as I was from one place and at the same time living in another. I wanted to meet someone who understood where I came from and might want to share in the adventure with me. So, I started connecting with potential mates in China. The idea was that we could have conversations online, or even over the phone, and then meet in person to see if there was a spark. It wasn't going to be a quick process, of course, but that wouldn't be a problem for someone with my tedious and persistent nature.

I started my search with several different candidates. I even traveled to China a couple of times. I discovered then what any teenager could now tell you: it's such a different thing to know someone online than it is to actually meet them in person. When the face-to-face visits began I realized I hadn't yet met anyone whom I thought I could spend the rest of my life with. Still, I tried not to be discouraged. I knew there had to be someone out there for me.

Finally, in 2000 I met Kathy (like me, my wife goes by an American name). In the beginning we had messaged each other back and forth, and then taken the tentative and stressful step of calling each other on the phone. Before long we were exchanging physical mail and fax messages, as well. Eventually I decided to meet with her in person, reserving a hotel near her apartment for just a week because I didn't intend to be away for very long. We hit it off, though, and I ended up extending my trip for a bit longer.

There was a lot to love about Kathy. Thankfully, she's quite a bit more open and outgoing than I am. Both of us are middle children in our families, and in her I discovered someone else who was also curious about the world. By the time I met her she was already living more than a thousand miles away from her hometown in northeast China, which made her something of a rarity. This was someone who wasn't going to be intimidated by the idea of living in a foreign country.

Shy as I was, I must have made enough of an impression to hold her interest. In 2001 we were married during the Lunar New Year. I traveled back to the US immediately, needing to resume my work. Kathy joined me several months later.

Obviously, we were both bound to go through a huge transition. I went from being a bachelor who spent much of his free time alone to a newlywed. Kathy had to make the same kind of change, along with all the geographic and cultural shifts I had already gone through, as well.

It wasn't an easy move for her. Although life in the USA is objectively nicer than it is in China in many different ways, change is always hard. When you're coming from a city, moving to a remote desert area can make things seem desolate and isolating. She had to overcome all those barriers while navigating a language gap *and* learning about her new and extremely stubborn husband.

Kathy adjusted, though, just as I had. In fact, she probably integrated more fully and quickly into American life. Before long she was picking up new English words and joining American social circles. There were few Chinese people in Los Alamos, and many of them could be found in the same local church on Friday night and Sunday. So, she started to attend their Friday night bible study group.

It wasn't long before our family started growing. First my daughter was born, and then my son followed a few years later. Suddenly, we were on track for a comfortable middle-class life. We had so many things we wouldn't have been able to dream about in China and it seemed as if we were settling into fresh routines that would remain comfortable and familiar for many years to come. I should have known by that point that life doesn't work that way. There were more transitions on the way.

I was overjoyed to have found a wife and started a family. Kathy brought a new sense of hope, purpose, and stability to my days. However, even though I was happier than ever, I couldn't have anticipated how certain small aspects of my new life would set me off on an entirely new path.

Cleanings and Conversions

It's amazing how things that seem like small details in a moment can turn out to be so consequential after the fact. If I had missed one or two questions on my college entrance exam I might have ended up as a laborer in China. Perhaps a wrong word, or poor clothing choice, might have derailed my plans to attend graduate school or move to America. Kathy could have ignored my simple message in an online chat, but her willingness to reply eventually turned into our marriage.

I could go on and on, but it usually turns out that huge

sections of our lives hinge on small decisions or coincidences that seem to come out of nowhere. That's how destiny works.

With that in mind, I can recall a handful of small twists and turns that took place over the next few years, each one shaping me into the scientist and entrepreneur I am today.

The first occurred when my wife decided to visit the dentist. Being slightly more worldly than I had been, she recognized that regular exams and cleanings were part of the normal routine in our new country. These procedures were even included in my job's dental insurance. Of course, American dentists had higher standards of care than she was used to in China. It wasn't long before they spotted some problems and were recommending fillings and crowns to her.

Kathy's dental work took several months to complete. Once she was finished, she did what any wife would have and suggested that I get my teeth checked out, as well. If you have followed me up to this point, you will already know I wasn't overly concerned about my oral health. That led me to ignore her helpful suggestions for months, right up until she took the initiative and made an appointment on my behalf. Now I *had* to go to the dentist.

The initial exam went as you might expect it would have. Once the hygienist began digging into the spaces between my teeth she asked whether I had ever flossed. I had to admit that it wasn't a regular habit. There was so much material in my teeth that she couldn't even finish the cleaning all in one session. She could only work at half of my mouth, and then I had to come back a week later so she could finish the job.

The result of all of this, naturally, was that the dentist implored me to start taking better care of my teeth. Regular brushing, flossing, and mouthwash were gently advised. I heard this suggestion every six months. It took many years, but I eventually fell into the habit. This small change to my daily routine made the dentist a lot more satisfied with his observation of my teeth on subsequent visits. More importantly, it led to a break-through later.

Kathy didn't just change my brushing and flossing routine. She worked to improve my spiritual health, as well. It wasn't long after my wife began attending church regularly in 2001 that she converted to the Christian faith. I didn't mind that she was embracing her religious side, but as a scientist I wasn't interested in participating. And so, each time she invited me to attend a service with her, I politely declined.

As it turned out, I wasn't the only persistent person living in my house. As the months went by, Kathy began dropping more hints about my lack of faith, leaving literature about Christian beliefs around the house, and (eventually) inviting clergy members to come and speak to me. In hindsight, I can see that she was concerned for both our marriage and my soul. I knew she wanted me to find my way to God, but I suspect she also sensed that I was becoming discontented with the path I had put myself on. I loved my family and enjoyed my work, but I had to wonder: after everything we had gone through, was a mundane and day-to-day existence our only reward?

As I moved through my thirties I became restless. I lost some of the innovative, hard-working edge that had made me so curious as a younger person. I put on weight and started to suffer from mild health elements like hypertension. I was, in essence, growing bored with the fabulous life we had built. I needed to fill the gap inside.

Despite that longing for something more, I didn't take immediate action. My conversion was a slower transition. At first, I simply continued to drive Kathy to Friday bible study. But gradually, instead of leaving and then returning to pick her up, I waited in the room and listened. I rarely spoke up or offered a challenging question; I was content to leave them with their faith.

Still, the gnawing sense that something was missing kept

eating away at me. In the spring of 2003, my wife and I were expecting our daughter. But somehow the wonder of life, and the prospect of a new beginning, was the furthest thing from my mind. I couldn't shake the feeling that I was missing out on a sense of destiny and purpose.

It was during this time that our church had its spring retreat. The congregation invited a visiting speaker, Pastor Zhang, to deliver a sermon. I don't remember much from the teachings that day. I simply recall that later on a Saturday afternoon Pastor Zhang and Hui Li, the leader of the Chinese fellowship group for Christians, came to visit our home. I'm not sure why they stopped by, but we ended up speaking together for a while. Eventually, Pastor Zhang asked me if I was ready to accept Jesus into my life. At that moment I lost all control. I began to cry and made my first prayer.

It took many attempts to convert the most stubborn of souls to his beliefs. And it required several *additional* years for me to truly absorb the shift into my heart and be open to the idea of a higher power working in my life.

When I finally called out to God for help, the first half of my life ended. The change didn't come overnight, of course, but in the years that followed I was spiritually reborn. That led me to an entirely different way of believing, naturally, but also a new framework for understanding science. It forced me to ask questions I hadn't considered before, which offered realizations about the nature of discovery that were previously hidden. That's a topic I hope to explore in a future book.

Why mention it in this title, then? This isn't a book about my faith, of course, but my conversion is central to my story. For one thing, becoming a Christian changed my worldview and personality. I found that I was more confident, more open, and better able to express myself. I have no doubt that I needed to find faith and purpose to become an entrepreneur. And for another thing, that religious conversion led to an important breakthrough moment in my career. It marked the beginning of my evolution from a scientist to a business owner.

The Slight Nudge of Destiny

As my family and spirit grew, God started to give me stronger and stronger hints about a new path to pursue.

The first change came during a transitional period in my career as a scientist. My team's work to create a general map of the human genome was coming to an end. That represented both a triumph and a challenge.

On the one hand, our years of tedious research had helped push the cause of human progress forward. We had laid the groundwork for future discoveries that could impact lives for decades to come. New cures and therapies might be unlocked, and future generations would have a basis of knowledge that would have been unavailable to us.

On a more practical level, however, meeting any scientific milestone can be a double-edged sword. If there aren't areas for further research that seem particularly obvious or necessary, you can actually put yourself out of work by making progress. Once the question you were hired to answer has been answered, you need to justify further expenses devoted to the same area.

In our case there seemed like a straightforward path ahead. As part of our project we had developed technology that would allow us to map and compare single-cell genomics. In case you aren't familiar with that term, it simply meant that we could look at different samples, like two yeast cells, and note the variations between them.

As a former physician, I retained a deep interest in the human biome. Several of the other researchers in our department wanted to work on human DNA, as well. Together, we started writing proposals for new studies that would look at the genomes available in human saliva. To do so meant familiarizing ourselves with dozens of previously published papers and studies on the subject. In the process we learned that many scientists and research departments around the world were asking questions about the meaning of the human oral biome.

Our goal was to take those efforts to the next stage. We wanted to ask even more specific questions, using the technology and methods we had been refining for years. In particular, we hoped to sequence hundreds of human saliva samples. Would they be similar, or different? And what would the diversity of life that can be found in human mouths tell us about various conditions and their treatments?

It would have been fascinating to get a chance to study specific bacteria and microcolonies under those circumstances. Unfortunately, none of our proposals were accepted, and the research wasn't funded. Still, the experience left me wondering what would happen if I were to look more deeply into the biome of the human mouth, nose, and throat. Maybe my curiosity was piqued by the scientific challenge. Or, maybe destiny was nudging me a bit more firmly.

I was getting hints about change at home, too. We discovered that my young son was being affected by hay fever and other seasonal ailments when he was a small child. This seemed puzzling to me, given that neither my wife nor I had ever suffered from a similar issue. Neither had I encountered allergic reactions very often as a doctor. I was aware that some people, like my father's friend, struggled with them but it wasn't a prevalent issue in my homeland. And even though I had a few friends at work who managed seasonal allergies, none of them seemed to be heavily affected.

My son was able to get by with some over-the-counter medications, so his allergies were more of a curiosity than a real problem. However, it wasn't long before I was reminded about them again.

The unlikely event was my son's fifth birthday. There were kids running around everywhere. All throughout our backyard there were children eating cake, playing games, and having a good time. The guests seemed to be enjoying themselves, save for one little girl. She couldn't manage to play because she was too busy scratching her arms and neck. Her habit of constantly digging into the affected areas with her tiny fingers wasn't helping. In fact, she was red all over and welts were forming on her skin. Still, she couldn't stop. The irritation was just too strong.

Later that evening, after the party had ended, my wife and I were speaking about the day. We talked about the poor girl's allergic reaction to the plants on our property and how bad we had felt for her. Then, my wife said: "Whoever solves the problem of allergies will be a very rich person." I told her it was not going to be easy as thousands of researchers had been studying the issue for several decades already. It was far from a sure thing that we would ever have a quick solution for allergies. As a matter of fact, we didn't have good answers for *most* chronic conditions.

Still, that thought hung over me like a cloud for several days. Allergy sufferers were becoming more common all around the world. Figuring out how to mitigate them would not only make a person wealthy, but also leave a positive impact on the world. I couldn't let go of the idea that *someone* should find a new way to treat sneezing and wheezing.

As intriguing as the idea was, I had too many other things going on in my life to hold on to the idea for too long. And besides, allergies weren't my area of research. Destiny was whispering to me now, but I still wasn't ready to listen. I was busy being a father and a scientist. If God wanted to get my attention he was going to have to be more direct... and he was.

My epiphany came at an event held by my church. We met

at Glorieta, a Christian conference center, with a nearby congregation from Albuquerque for a special presentation. Our guest that day was a pastor from China. He recounted his difficult journey through medical school, advancement into the field of heart surgery, and ultimate conversion to Christianity.

As he wove his story together, I felt small tears coming to my eyes. It was surprising. Although I had developed a very strong sense of faith by that point, I rarely found myself feeling so struck by my emotions. It almost seemed as if I were crying in spite of myself. Could it be that the nature of his story, which felt so close to my own, was stirring up deep emotions inside me? I didn't have the sense that I was affected in that way, but there was nothing else to explain the moment. Whatever the cause, my weeping just wouldn't stop. After a few minutes I decided it might be best if I went outside the church to regain my composure.

I had expected a short break to give me control of my body and emotions, but the opposite happened: the tears started coming with greater intensity. I didn't feel sad, or even joyful, and yet I couldn't stop my eyes from watering. If anything, I was worried about the possibility I might start to sob, given that I could feel congestion building in my nose. I wondered: what had broken in my soul to trigger such an unexpected outpouring? How could I be so touched when my mind felt cheerful?

That was the moment when I realized God might have been playing a small trick on me. The story the speaker offered us *was* gripping, but his tale wasn't the source of my discomfort. I was having an allergic reaction. The church was surrounded by fields of spring pollen. Those fields, more than any spiritual revelation, were causing me trouble at that moment. Looking back, though, I have to wonder whether my higher power wasn't speaking to me all the same. After all, that moment has affected me deeply for years afterward. It has also allowed me to affect the lives of so many others.

In the following months, two things happened. First, my allergies got much worse. Eventually, I reached a point where I couldn't even breathe through my nose at night. That wrecked my sleep and gave me a sore throat that would persist for months at a time.

And second, I *finally* started to take the idea of studying allergies seriously. I'd had many hints, nudges, and reminders up to that point in my life, but each of them had been easy enough to ignore. Now I had a problem I could no longer ignore. As a medical professional and researcher, I wasn't sure if I might be able to get to the bottom of the problem, but I was sure I would not figure anything out if I didn't start it. Besides, I was finally in a place in my career where I could think about a new challenge.

Because my department's participation in the Human Genome Project had come to a close not long before my "allergy conversion," I had been reassigned to another part of the organization that involved safety and quality study. This was important work, but not something I was well-suited for. The data of organization and human performance is very different from the data you get from a lab. Both the measurements and conclusions tend to be more subjective than objective.

While I endeavored to learn about the basics of safety and organizational standards, my natural skill set was in more clinical work. As a new Christian I had to wonder why God had given me such a difficult assignment while also burdening me with allergies. Only later did I see that He had a plan. The lessons I learned during that time became invaluable when I began designing my own studies and became immersed in topics like quality control and supply chain management.

That hindsight wasn't available to me then, however, and I struggled to find meaning in my work. With a new sense of inspiration, and a lot of uncomfortable symptoms, I began searching for different projects that would allow for continued research into allergies that aligned with my work at the Department of Energy. No matter which avenue I pursued, or who I talked to, I couldn't find the right fit. There were lots of people studying human reactions to pollen and other irritants, but my part of the government wasn't interested in funding further research into that area. There was the sense that allergies were *interesting* but not necessarily relevant to our specialties.

It won't surprise you to know that I didn't give up on my new obsession. I started studying the history and prevalence of allergies on my own time, and attended conferences put together by the National Institutes of Health (which was located nearby) whenever possible.

Before long I learned that allergies aren't necessarily caused by the factors we tend to expect.

4

THE HYGIENE HYPOTHESIS

I mentioned early on that this book isn't really about me. Even though the first few chapters gave you a glimpse into my life, it's because my journey informs my point of view. It helped me see things in a way that other doctors or scientists might not have. But much of the *really* interesting work began long before I was ever involved.

This is our chance to catch up with some of that work. In this chapter I want to turn your attention towards a scientific realignment that has been quietly unfolding for the past few decades. You may or may not be aware of it, but everything we know about germs, bacteria, and even healthy living is being reconsidered by a field of study that began with the *hygiene hypothesis*.

So often, in science and history, we learn new things that seem obvious after the fact. They come across as fitting in with common sense even though it took someone – or maybe many people – to make the connections clear. That has been the case with the hygiene hypothesis. When it comes to allergies and autoimmune disorders, the truth may have been hiding in plain sight all along.

To understand why, we need to look at the march of human progress from a different point of view than the one we normally adopt.

Humans live, on average, decades longer than they used to. That's largely due to the fact that we have learned a lot about germs, viruses, and bacteria over the past couple of centuries. As technology has grown and society has advanced, things have gotten cleaner and cleaner. We have gone from defecating in fields and bathing ourselves in dirty rivers to using soap, sanitizing our drinking water, and even deploying antibiotics against microbial attackers.

All of this has made life easier to maintain. That's obvious from any study of medical history, and something I can attest to as a doctor, scientist, and accidental time traveler. As you move from one era of understanding to the next, things generally get cleaner and less dangerous. That's why few of us die from minor wounds or suffer from parasites in the Western world. Neither do we routinely perish from simple diseases that used to bring death to millions every decade. Cuts that would become infected, or sicknesses that might have the potential to reach a critical point, are held back by routine cleaning and basic first aid.

All of this is undoubtedly positive. No one would want to return to an age when things like my old friend Mercury Red were used in abundance. However, it turns out that our progress towards a cleaner and cleaner world might have some unexpected side effects. And not all of them make modern life better.

What's Wrong With Being Squeaky Clean?

What if cleanliness isn't always next to godliness? What if an over-sterilized world has side effects we might not have foreseen or considered? Researchers have begun asking these questions in the past few decades. As it turns out, there might be some reason for concern.

Consider this: although recorded human history only goes back a few thousand years (with much of that being fragmented), biologists can demonstrate that early humans have been around for much, much longer. In fact, if you count our primate ancestors, we've been roaming the planet for millions of journeys around the sun.

When you look at time on that scale, you find that even basic forms of hygiene like hand washing have only come around very recently. Most of our forebears lived and died in a world that was very, *very* dirty. Earlier humans lived in conditions where they had close contact with wild animals, drank unfiltered water from streams and lakes, and were regularly exposed to microbial dangers like feces and insect bites.

That probably doesn't sound pleasant to you, and I can't imagine it was much fun for them, either. The prevailing conditions were gritty, and huge numbers of our would-be ancestors got sick and died with regularity. The ones who lived, though, got by with immune systems that were very attuned to certain biological threats. Not only were there the hygiene-related risks associated with things like undercooked meat, uncleaned vegetables, and animal waste, but also pathogens spread through other ways like malaria and dengue fever that have been with us for millennia.

Over time, humans learned to clean up our environments. Our bodies, however, have stayed vigilant, looking for new threats around every corner. How could they not, after hundreds of thousands of years of evolution had shown that serious illness could show up unexpectedly at any moment?

This leads us to the basic theory behind the hygiene hypothesis. In essence, it says that our immune systems, in an environment that lacks the traditional dangers they evolved to conquer, will begin to mistake other forms of stimuli for disease and overreact. That overreaction can show up in many ways, with common allergies being the most visible symptom.

This simple idea is completely intuitive, but it stands in contrast to the way most people think about science, not to mention their own bodies. Generally, the public thinks in terms of bacteria being bad and wanting their immune systems to be as strong as possible. In reality, many could be experiencing difficulties precisely *because* their immune systems have been given too much power. They have many tools for fighting pathogens, but those pathogens have been driven away.

For a rough analogy, imagine a police unit that is used to fighting vicious gangs armed with automatic weapons in a large city. Suppose you were to increase their funding, give them new equipment, and then set them loose to solve crimes in a small, quiet retirement community. How long do you think it would take for them to see dangers that didn't actually exist? And what sorts of accidents might result from those misunderstandings?

This is a very simple way of explaining a large and complex system, of course, but hopefully it paints a picture in your mind that is easy to understand. Having a cleaner world has brought us an untold number of benefits. It has also likely prevented billions of unnecessary early deaths. It's possible, however, that in our rush to eradicate every germ or microbe in our immediate vicinity, we have gone too far. We have put our immune systems in environments that are too sterilized to allow them to function normally.

It's worth pointing out once again that if you weren't already familiar with the hygiene hypothesis, then all of this can seem like a strange theory. Many readers will have been hearing about the dangers of germs and bacteria for their whole lives, so it can seem strange to suggest that dirt, grime, or parasites can have even tertiary health benefits. Luckily, we have a growing body of scientific work that backs up some of the basic tenets.

The Science of Dirt and Germs

The hygiene hypothesis gets its roots from a paper by David Strachan, a British epidemiologist. He was one of the first to suggest we might be overprotecting ourselves from Mother Nature. Specifically, he noted in a 1989 study that children who came from bigger families tended to have fewer allergy symptoms. Subsequent research suggested that perhaps having groups of kids together made things less sanitary.

As any parent can tell you, this matches up perfectly with everyday observation. The more children you have in a confined area, the more dirt and germs you're going to find.

Before long, these insights led to more work around the correlation between hygiene and allergic symptoms. For instance, roughly a decade later Dr. Erika von Mutius studied the differences between allergies and asthma in East Germany and West Germany. Her expectation, consistent with the prevailing wisdom of the time, was that the East Germans would have more problems. After all, they had more economic and environmental burdens to deal with. Their air and water weren't as clean. The assumption was that these poor conditions would lead to more allergy symptoms and more suffering. Common sense said that dirtier environments would likely lead to poorer health outcomes.

However, her study showed just the opposite. It was the West German kids, with better air and cleaner homes, who were suffering from allergies at a higher rate. Astonished, her team looked at comparisons from other areas. Before long, a clear trend began to emerge: the richer your city or country was, the more likely you were to develop allergies.

In another study, scientific observers found that one area of Europe had dramatically lower rates of allergy than a nearby population with the same climate, genetics, and recent history. For most of the past few centuries, the Karelia region was located within Sweden. But, during World War II it was absorbed by the Soviet Union, and later continued as part of Russia when the USSR collapsed.

As a result, a group of people who are genetically similar to their neighbors in Sweden are now part of Russia. One set lives in the relative wealth of Sweden, the other in less-prosperous Russia. What makes them interesting to proponents of the hygiene hypothesis is that rates of allergy and associated autoimmune disorders are several times higher on the Swedish side. In fact, the divergence in health outcomes can be traced precisely to the 1940s. Allergy rates only begin to move apart in the years *after* that point.

The question facing researchers, once again, amounted to: what is it about economic prosperity that makes people so sensitive to pollen and other allergens?

After combing through dozens of genetic markers and lifestyle factors, scientists felt confident they had located a simple difference. Namely that those on the (now) Russian side of the border were drinking water from a nearby lake, while those on the Swedish side had water that was much more heavily treated with antibacterial chemicals and UV rays. The Russian water contained nine times the number of microbes as the Swedish water, activating immune responses within the body. On the Swedish side, the cleaner water was free of that material, suggesting the residents' immune systems never found the threats it was looking for. So, it started to attack innocuous materials, confusing them for dangerous invaders.

As more and more scientists became interested in the relationship between dirt, money, and allergies, further connections were discovered. In particular, numerous sets of data suggested that these sorts of immunological differences began in the womb. That is, that your likelihood of developing allergies was largely determined before you were even born. Having a mother who was exposed to certain types of pathogens, such as those you might find working on a farm, for example, gave you more protection.

These observations might have been controversial at the time, but they make perfect sense in the context of the other things we know about biology. As a rule, all living things adapt to their environments. They also change characteristics based on the demands that are put upon them. A person who takes up running will develop the ability to propel themselves farther and faster with repeated effort. Someone who gets up early every day will start to feel like a morning person. These are small adaptations that become apparent over time.

The same thing happens with our immunity, and particularly in the earliest stages of life. If your pregnant mother was caring for horses, being bitten by mosquitoes on a daily basis, and drinking unpasteurized milk straight from the pail, then could it really be surprising that your immune system would emerge ready to take on pathogens associated with hay, insects, or raw milk? Conversely, if your pre-birth months were spent in a largely sterile environment, might your body not mistake peanuts or pollen for ancestral enemies that it wanted to protect you from but hadn't actually seen before?

With time, more studies like these came to the attention of the scientific community. The evidence began to add up. Wealth and, in particular, cleanliness were tied to allergic dispositions. This led to more sampling, new research projects, and a greater sense that eradicating microbes wasn't necessarily as important as keeping them in balance.

While the hygiene hypothesis represented a breakthrough moment in modern science, it's important to point out that this knowledge didn't arrive all at once. Not only did the results pile up over years, but study is still ongoing. In fact, we are still working out the finer points and probably will be for many more years. Just as cleanliness isn't bad, the hygiene hypothesis certainly doesn't suggest that all germs are good, or that you should necessarily seek out exposure to dangerous illnesses. Remember, some of the microbes out there are the same pathogens that killed billions of earlier humans. Besides, it isn't necessarily more germs that we need to protect us from certain allergies or illnesses, but more so it's the right kind of germs in the right locations with sufficient nutritions (more on this in a bit).

One particularly troublesome byproduct of the hygiene hypothesis has been a misunderstanding around vaccines. While there have been fears in some corners that vaccinating children could harm their immune systems or lead to developmental disabilities (like autism), this isn't supported by research. Also, one could reasonably say that the risks associated with the kinds of illnesses we vaccinate against are more significant.

The point isn't to debate vaccination science, however. It's simply to show that the hygiene hypothesis represents a relatively new way to think about immunity and allergies. It struck me as a novel idea when I first heard of it, and one that matched up with my own experiences. After all, allergies were virtually unknown in my part of rural China where people hadn't even known to use toothbrushes.

. . .

Scrubbing My Mind of Old Science

I first learned about the hygiene hypothesis sometime after the publication of the David Strachan paper. Although his research wasn't directly relevant to my study in genetics, or my work on the Human Genome Project, it nevertheless fell within my general area of knowledge. When someone makes a bold claim in your area of science, it's hard not to notice.

As the years went by, more and more papers and research projects came around, each one building on the basic premise. Eventually, the data that was presented – not to mention my own experiences in China, where allergies *and* hygiene standards were largely unknown – had convinced me the theory had merit.

I wasn't the only one. The National Institutes of Health, which also has offices in New Mexico, started hosting seminars that included hygiene hypothesis studies. I made a point of attending them when I could, especially after my son started displaying allergy symptoms of his own. Although his sniffles were mild, as a father I wanted to know if there were steps I could take to ease his suffering. As a scientist and medical professional, it felt like all the tools I needed to crack the code were right in front of me.

My early research didn't get much further than a bit of reading and a few seminars, though. Eventually, I would always be pulled to another task, usually one that was closer to my role at the Department of Energy. So, I maintained a casual interest in new hygiene hypothesis developments and the study of allergies, but let them recede into the background of life.

All of that changed dramatically about a decade later. First came the bestselling book, *An Epidemic of Absence*, by Moises Velasquez-Manoff. His work popularized the hygiene hypothesis and made it accessible to those without medical or scientific backgrounds. This reignited the interest in allergies both within and outside the medical community.

Next came the allergic attack during our church retreat. At that point, my own suffering, combined with the lack of direction in my career, pushed me to start studying allergies more seriously. Given that I could barely breathe or sleep, the problem became too pressing to ignore. I started to wonder what answers could be found by taking the hygiene hypothesis further, or whether there were key parts of the process that were being overlooked.

It was time to put my stubborn mind fully to work on a new problem.

5

EXPLORING ALLERGIES

In the beginning of this book, I told you one of my deepest beliefs is that everything is connected. In fact, much of what we think about as "good" or "bad" is dependent on context. As an example, Mercury Red is a great antibacterial swab for most people. For me, it's a kind of low-grade poison. Likewise, stubbornness and persistence are part of the same neurological process. The personality trait that had made it difficult for me to make friends and get along with teachers at school was about to become my biggest asset as I looked for relief from allergies.

In the months after my initial allergy attack I grew more frantic for answers. It wasn't just that I wanted to solve the puzzle; I was *suffering*.

My allergy symptoms became so severe that my nose was stuffy all the time. That made it difficult to breathe, even at night. Before too long I had developed a habit of sleeping propped up on pillows with my mouth open. I woke up constantly when I should have been deep asleep. Even worse, I developed an intensely sore throat that never seemed to heal. It wasn't healthy to breathe the dry New Mexico air through my mouth at all hours, but I didn't have any choice.

Allergies were turning my life upside down. I decided it was time to fight back against them, using the knowledge and skills life had given me.

I started as any scientist would: by digging into books and articles. My research began with traditional allergy treatments and those suggested by the hygiene hypothesis. I wasn't quite convinced that wealth and soap were the cause for modern health problems – having lived without both in the past and seen the results. But there did seem to be *something* to the notion that certain afflictions were on the rise in richer parts of the world.

A deeper review of the scientific literature from that time led me to a paper by David Hutchins. By studying immigrants to Italy, he found that most who developed allergies did so within the first 3 to 5 years of arriving in their new country. That suggested some sort of environmental or lifestyle factor, but it didn't seem to aid me in my analysis. After all, I'd been in America for 17 years at that point. Any changes in my exposure to pollen, food, or new climate conditions that would have generated an allergic reaction should have affected me long before that point.

With those obvious candidates out of the way I kept searching my brain for the answer to one simple question: *what had changed?*

Looking for an Unconventional Answer

It didn't take me long to rule out the conventional or accepted suspected allergy causes. My immigration was too far in the past; I was well-adapted to life in the US. Nothing had changed significantly at home or work so far as my natural environment was concerned. We didn't have any new plants, I hadn't changed my soap or bathing habits, and we hadn't picked up any new foods or fabrics.

I briefly considered that some aspect of climate change might be involved, with pollen migrating from one area to another, but dismissed that theory based on the observation that others weren't being affected. Besides, there didn't seem to be anything new growing in my neighborhood.

The more I thought about things, the more I became convinced that something had changed with me. That was when I thought back to my research proposals and realized there *was* something different about my life in the months leading up to my allergic attack.

You might recall that my wife adjusted more quickly to Western life than I had. She was the first one of us to start going to the dentist regularly, eventually persuading me to go as well. It had only been a few months before my allergy attack that I had started brushing, flossing, and using mouthwash regularly. Those may all sound like good things, but they also had the effect of suddenly making my mouth more sterile. The bacteria that had been living in my gums and throat for more than forty years were removed almost all at once.

With this realization I started thinking about the hygiene hypothesis in a different way. Could it have been the case that removing bacteria from my mouth or throat had actually made me more susceptible to allergies? The idea seemed to run contrary to most of the prevailing wisdom at the time, but it also made a kind of sense. Nothing else in my environment or lifestyle seemed to account for the change. It was as if a hidden switch had been flipped when I wasn't looking.

The only way to test the idea would be to get some data to work with.

The ideal method would have been to secure a grant for a

large study through the Department of Energy. However, I already knew from my previous experience that getting funding would be an enormous challenge. Even though it was obvious to me that finding a new form of allergy relief could change lives and enhance scientific understanding at the same time, I didn't have enough proof to get the kind of support that would be needed to pay for my own research at the lab. I certainly wouldn't be able to involve my colleagues.

I was surrounded by some of the world's brightest minds and best scientific equipment. Unfortunately, I couldn't use any of it to find the allergy cure I needed for myself and others.

With that avenue seemingly closed for the time being, I turned to my second course of action: experimenting on myself.

There is a long tradition of scientists and doctors serving as their own guinea pigs. Usually, this happens when ideas or research methods are either far beyond the mainstream or decades ahead of conventional wisdom. In my case, it was just the cheapest and most accessible option. If I couldn't get funding and support for a large-scale study, I could at least understand what was happening in my own body.

There was also a practical advantage to studying myself. While having hundreds of volunteers might have given me a *wide* perspective, looking intensely at my own test results would allow me to go *deep* over time. I could look at any aspect of my own health that I wanted without having to worry about keeping track of the sorts of external factors that might affect a bigger study.

In a perfect world, I would have begun the process by comparing older, pre-allergy samples to newer samples taken after my symptoms had appeared. The only problem was that materials and records didn't exist. If I would have had the fore-thought to create and save some at the time when I was immersed in studying saliva for our single-cell genomics proposals, the task in front of me would have been easier.

Instead, I would have to begin after the fact and hope to make new connections.

I started by taking all I knew about allergies, bacteria, and the hygiene hypothesis and searching for different variables I could measure and control. I wanted to follow a scientific process, even if my "pilot study" was going to be on the smallest possible scale. So, I found a lab that could do diagnostic work for me as a private citizen rather than a Department of Energy employee.

Realizing that I couldn't let any more time get away, I started collecting my own saliva and stool samples immediately. The goal was to find the link, if any, between changes in my microbiome and my allergy symptoms. As you can probably imagine, our internal health can be altered by many different things, such as a change in diet or habits. To reduce variation within my sampling I followed strict procedures – for example, collecting saliva first thing in the morning before any eating, drinking, or oral hygiene.

I didn't know if I'd be able to find a connection between my microbiome and my allergic reactions, or how long it might take to get the results I needed. I just had to have patience and trust that God would show me the way. I took both saliva and stool samples because I was working on the theory that the oral and intestinal biomes were closely connected. That turns out to be true in some circumstances and less relevant in others.

As I was starting to gather information, I also began searching for possible connections and solutions. I was convinced, by that point, that the hygiene hypothesis had some merits. And, I felt like it was only a matter of time before I could prove that changes to oral hygiene could have an impact on allergies. But there were still a lot of missing pieces.

Certain pieces of research on the hygiene hypothesis suggested that more bacteria in my mouth might shift my immune response elsewhere. Other studies suggested bacteria diversity could be the key, and that I simply needed more variety in my oral biome. There were even some researchers who thought that parasites, and controlled environments, could be the real key. The literature gave me lots of theories to work with, but nothing like the whole picture. I had ideas without answers.

In order to start gathering hard data towards a solution, I decided to run a series of experiments on my own body. Since I suspected that a change in dental cleaning habits had led to my allergic reactions – and because I was already suffering – I decided to do something drastic. I stopped brushing, flossing, and using mouthwash altogether.

I'm certainly not recommending you give up oral hygiene. I didn't intend to do so permanently myself. I just wanted to know whether I could reverse a process I was sure had taken place in my mouth.

The experience was not entirely comfortable. For one thing, any change in your daily habits and routines is going to feel strange. And of course, there were worries that I might be undoing the hard work of my dentist and his team. Thankfully, I can report that my teeth didn't fall out of my head. At the same time, I wouldn't be able to describe the effort as a success, either.

What essentially happened was that I gave up brushing and flossing for a few weeks at a time. During those periods bacteria would indeed grow in my mouth, to the point that my gums would become red and inflamed. After a while, infections would spring up in my jaw, causing chronic pain. Meanwhile my allergy symptoms weren't improving at all. Eventually I would give up, continue my oral hygiene routine, and see the pain and swelling disappear. Then, after my mouth was feeling better, I would start the process all over again.

It took a few attempts before I gave up on this particular

line of research. Whatever was going on, it wasn't going to be cured by throwing away my toothbrush.

Sore Throats and Setbacks

As the end of spring 2014 arrived, my hopes of finding a solution started to wane. My symptoms certainly weren't improving much even as the summer came. Eventually, I had to accept my allergies were not seasonal as with many people who get allergies the first time. My allergic rhinitis started as a persistent one. I felt certain there was something to the intersection of the hygiene hypothesis and my observations on oral hygiene. And yet, the scientist in me had to conclude I wasn't making any progress on my theories. It seemed as if I were wasting my time, not to mention my money, on a theory that wasn't going anywhere.

The months went by and I got the opportunity to perform a kind of natural experiment. Kathy and I decided that when spring break came around in 2015 we would take our children to Italy for a vacation. At the very least it seemed like I could get away from the juniper pollen that was tormenting me for a couple of weeks. It wasn't a permanent solution, but I was eager for any relief, or just a new perspective on my problem.

The trip itself was enjoyable, and my allergy symptoms were indeed less severe. However, I still felt congested most of the time, and especially in the evenings. I realized that whatever had changed for me probably couldn't be escaped by traveling to a different part of the world, or by simply getting away from the allergens that bothered me at home.

With that reality in mind I switched my tactics. Instead of looking for answers, I began searching for treatments. I stopped collecting samples for myself and looked for treatments that could help me live and sleep more comfortably. I was still committed to learning about the causes of allergy symptoms, but also recognized finding answers could be a long-term challenge. In the meantime, I needed a way to get through the night and deal with my aching throat.

The roots of a makeshift solution started with a simple realization: at night, I could breathe more comfortably if I held a blanket or towel over my face. Doing so kept in a bit of the warmth and moisture that would normally escape when I opened my mouth. Things were even better if I wet the cloth beforehand. It dried itself after a couple of hours, but in the meantime I could find some relief.

There was a big problem with this quick fix. Namely that I needed it most when I was sleeping, but couldn't lie still with a wet blanket on my face while in bed. It wasn't easy to keep in place, especially if I moved. So, I started experimenting and eventually designed a cloth mask that I could wear safely and comfortably in bed. It would go dry in the night, just as any towel or blanket would, but it gave me a chance to get some rest and heal my throat.

Certainly, I would have preferred an allergy cure to a few hours of sleep with a homemade mask on my mouth, but I was thankful for any kind of improvement. Besides, my saliva research hadn't been showing any results. It seemed as if there was nothing left for me to do but accept my fate and live through it the best I could.

Luckily for me, life has a funny way of giving you a nudge just when it feels like you have no way to move forward.

A False Dawn

Late in 2015, after years of allergy suffering, something amazing happened. One morning in the summer, I simply woke up and realized I had slept flat, off the high pillow, without any symptoms. It was like I'd never had allergies to begin with. I could even enjoy sleeping on my belly, my default sleeping position, for the next several days.

Obviously, I was thankful for the relief. As a scientist and medical professional, however, the whole situation was perplexing. I couldn't think of anything in my lifestyle that had changed. I wasn't eating new foods or traveling to new places. I hadn't tried any different medicines, and had even given up my experiments of cutting back on oral hygiene. It was true that I wasn't brushing my teeth as often in those days, but I wasn't going weeks between cleanings as I had when I thought it might stop me from sneezing.

There didn't seem to be any discernible cause for my condition to change. In the back of my mind I knew from studies that some allergy sufferers inexplicably got better. They simply "grew out" of their symptoms. No one really knew why, but that didn't bother me at the time. I was simply glad to live like a normal person without the unending burdens of runny noses and watery eyes. I hoped my relief would last forever.

At the same time, the researcher in me wanted to know what happened. My allergy symptoms had improved. What caused it? Had my oral microbiome caused it or changed at the same time? I started taking saliva samples again, hoping I might be able to compare the data with previous observations to find a cause.

My optimism turned out to be short-lived in both cases. Not only was I unable to determine what had caused my symptoms to recede (I never did), but they didn't stay away forever. In fact, in the spring of 2016 they returned with more fury than ever. It felt as if I were allergic to *everything*, with physical reactions that were even stronger than before. I kept taking samples of my saliva, but I wasn't sure what to look for... or even what to expect in the future. Would my allergies just keep getting worse and worse? Would I ever understand why my body was attacking pollen in what felt like a life-or-death struggle?

I still wanted answers, but more than that I wanted a way to live with my condition. And so, that's when I put my limited entrepreneurial experience back to work.

With allergies keeping my sleep short and my throat raw, I decided to resume working on my wet mask. After experimenting with different materials and ways of placing the wet cloth over my face in a manner that didn't completely suffocate me, I realized something: there were probably other people out there suffering from the same exact issue. Why couldn't I take what I had learned from my own trial and error process and come up with a nighttime sleep mask for allergy sufferers?

The result was a product I called *Knoze Jr. (or little nose)*. It launched in 2016 and was marketed locally as a wet mask for those who were trying to survive the same allergy-related sore throat symptoms I was.

I had two goals when I put the Knoze masks on the market. First, I wanted to share something I had invented with others who could benefit from it. Second, I had hoped to reinvest the profits towards proving my theories on allergies and saliva.

Discovering a Dead End

One of the beautiful things about science, and the nature of persistent effort as a whole, is that the biggest triumphs can eventually come from the worst setbacks. It's fortunate for me that things work that way because in the autumn of 2016, life, and my own impatience, were making it difficult for me to see a way ahead. Luckily God helped carry me through a very difficult time.

The trouble started when I implemented what might have been the worst-designed study I had ever heard of, much less participated in. Without any funding or outside guidance, I was facing a conundrum: how could I gather and analyze data without money to pay for it? I had already gotten around the problem once by experimenting on myself and taking my own saliva samples. Now, I decided to take the next step with a pilot study and analyze six months' worth of information – three from when my allergies were persistent and another three from the time when my allergies became seasonal.

As a scientist, I knew that any data I could glean from such a small sample set would almost certainly be statistically irrelevant. There just wasn't enough information to work with. However, I was looking to save money and had hoped I might stumble across an insight that would guide me towards a bigger and more meaningful analysis.

It wasn't perfect, but I did at least have a direction to pursue. My attempts to reduce allergy symptoms by ignoring oral hygiene had already failed. The hygiene hypothesis suggested I might have better luck in studying the diverse city of bacteria in my mouth. In other words, I stopped worrying that I might be *missing* something in my saliva, and instead determined that there might not be *enough* of a specific bacteria. Of course, I couldn't find out by guessing. I would need some actual numbers to look at.

With that goal fixed in my mind I found a lab that was willing to sequence microbiomes of stool and saliva for me. The tests would be expensive, but not so costly that I was willing to ignore my curiosity. So, I packaged up the material, sent it away, and waited a month for the results.

Eventually the lab sent me back the raw data. That's where my skills as a researcher came in. I'd been studying the human genome, bacterial genomes, and microbiomes for years at that point, and knew how to analyze specific sequences of a biome for myself. I was very familiar with the tools and datasets I would be looking at, and went straight to my computer to look for results.

There were huge volumes of observations to work through. Even though I had only used six samples, each one could register between 500 and 800 different bacteria strains of varying abundance. Simply looking at them directly made it impossible to spot trends, so I had to generate before-and-after tables to get a better picture of what had been happening in my mouth.

What I wanted to find, of course, was an obvious explanation for the differences in my symptoms. And that's exactly what I found when running computer-assisted comparisons. I discovered there were three specific bacteria that stood out. None of them was especially rare, but neither were they abundant. More importantly, the three were only present in any real quantities after my allergies had subsided.

It looks, finally, as if I had the answer I was searching for. The hygiene hypothesis had led me towards a commonsense solution. My oral biome just needed more diversity. One of these bacteria, or maybe all three of them together, seemed to be pacifying my immune system and reducing my allergy symptoms. All I had to do was verify what I had learned and study it a bit further.

With this imagined breakthrough in my mind I found a new sense of enthusiasm for the project. I started collecting more samples from my family in order to trace where the three novel bacteria came from. I didn't just want to learn about my biome, but also understand why my son had allergies while my wife and daughter did not. I took it all – the previous samples

I'd collected, along with the new ones from my family – and mailed them off to another lab.

This time I wanted answers. That meant I wasn't sparing any expense. So, in addition to reporting on the results of the testing, I also paid for this lab to run computational analysis for me. I knew that digging through the resulting data would be several times more rigorous than what I had already done and didn't want to spend weeks or months getting to the outcomes I expected. It would be better, I figured, for them to do the calculations and give me the good news straightaway.

When the reports came back I could barely wait the few minutes it took to download them. There was raw data, advanced statistics, and plenty of cross-reference tabs. I knew exactly what I was looking for, however, so I went straight to the side-by-side comparisons of the three bacteria I had been examining.

I scanned the pages furiously, finally locating the conclusions I was so desperate for. What did they tell me? Nothing. The bacteria were *everywhere*. They could be found in all the samples, including my own that were taken before and after my allergic episodes. Not only that, but they were found in almost the same volume throughout. I was staring at complete statistical noise.

Surely, I thought, there must be something missing in the data analysis. I opened the individual data files for each record and started looking at the tables manually. The raw numbers told the same story, even though I didn't want to believe it. The bacteria I had been looking for were virtually unchanged in every cycle.

The realization was so hurtful I almost found it difficult to breathe. Stunned as I was, I went back to my first six months of statistical analysis and opened the raw files I had originally begun working with. What I found only served to increase my pain. Somehow the early conclusions I had come to regarding these three bacteria were all wrong. Either the software hadn't tabulated them in the way I had expected, or I had made a computational error in my functions.

Filled with fury and grief, I didn't even bother to check. It just didn't matter at that point. I had been chasing the statistical version of a mirage.

My excitement quickly turned to depression. I realized at that moment that I had wasted three years looking for answers I couldn't find. That time was gone, and so was the sum of money I had spent on labs and data analysis. Even worse, the company had discarded my samples after sequencing them, meaning it would be impossible for me to send them elsewhere.

In other words, everything was gone and I had gotten nowhere. My theory related to the hygiene hypothesis couldn't be advanced. I couldn't afford a new study and didn't have any material to work with. The wet mask product I had introduced to the market was beset by problems. And don't forget, I still didn't have any solution to the allergic symptoms that made it difficult for me to live, breathe, and sleep.

My dreams of advancing allergy science and becoming a successful entrepreneur were crashing down around me. I fell into a depression that would linger for months.

6

A NEW THEORY OF ALLERGY RELIEF

One of the most amazing things about science, not to mention the journey of life, is that it can feel like you have no hope even as you're on the verge of a breakthrough. Sometimes you're right on the edge of a big discovery, or a new way of seeing things, just as you feel like giving up.

I certainly didn't have any sense I was on track to have any scientific discovery of significance during the last few months of 2016. As weeks turned into months I couldn't shake off the feeling of disappointment that lingered with me each day. My study and efforts had come to nothing. It seemed as if my struggle to better understand allergies was coming to an unsuccessful close. I decided to chalk the whole thing up to a learning experience and move on.

There was just one thing I had to do before I could close the book on that chapter of my life: I needed to report my failures to the rest of the scientific community. If I had accomplished one thing, it was figuring out that seasonal allergies were probably not related to the oral microbiome. By putting together a brief report with my methods and conclusions I could, at the very least, prevent someone else from duplicating my errors or following a dead end in the research.

So, I went back to the data sets once more. This time I didn't pay much attention to the conclusions, just the information that had been provided to me. I wasn't really looking for answers, just to better explain how I had gotten things so wrong. My hope was that it might save some other researcher a great deal of time and energy later.

Hidden in Plain Sight

AFTER A FEW MONTHS away from the project, I found I could examine the data with fresh eyes. And, having already accepted that the conclusions I wanted weren't available, I was able to study the facts and figures in a more dispassionate way. I wasn't tied to an outcome, which made it easier to just examine the numbers. Perhaps that's why something new attracted my curiosity.

I had asked the second lab to analyze and compute any differences between the samples that were taken when I was having allergies versus the ones that were collected when I wasn't. Specifically, I wanted them to tabulate the bacteria counts before and after. They helpfully included a table showing the variability within each time frame, along with any correlations that seemed statistically significant.

With all the observations in a large spreadsheet, I started to look for P value correlations across multiple inputs. In other words, I started to ask myself whether there were more complicated relationships that needed to be studied (or potentially ruled out). Specifically, I was looking at the comparison of each group of bacteria across the two sets of samples, before and after my allergies got better in summer 2015.

To better understand what I was seeing, I changed the layout of the information slightly. And with that, a simple reordering of data within a spreadsheet, the truth came out.

It only took a few moments to realize two types of bacteria were reduced during my worst allergic attacks. They were called *Streptococcus* and *Veillonella*.

I decided to do some online research on each of them. I knew they were common but didn't have much insight into how they worked within the body.

I learned that both had been studied since the 1950s, and that certain variations of Streptococcus can cause infections of the throat (and occasionally worse). However, at the right level the "good" variety can live in your mouth and throat without causing any damage whatsoever. The same goes for Veillonella. Although too much of the wrong type can lead to sickness, it is a generally innocuous strain of bacteria that lives in any healthy human being's mouth.

None of what I saw made them seem like interesting suspects for the purposes of allergy research. Still, I found it intriguing that these two types of bacteria were more abundant during the periods when my immune system was calmer. I asked myself whether that detail could be important. Could either of them have a hidden property I wasn't aware of?

I couldn't make any connection in my mind. I also knew that both of these bacteria had been studied extensively in the past. Surely, if either one of them was crucial to human immune system function, it would have been noticed decades ago. After years of wasted money and effort I certainly wasn't interested in pursuing another loose thread of study that would go nowhere. So, I made a note of the interesting connection for the paper I planned to write and then left the research for another day.

It wasn't until a few weeks later that I thought to pursue the idea further. I was working on some household chores when the inspiration suddenly arrived in my mind: why shouldn't I research those two bacteria together? Perhaps they had a relationship with each *other* that could make a difference.

I think God was whispering to me at that moment. Mere minutes into my online research I discovered I had been asking the wrong questions about Streptococcus and Veillonella. Although they were known to be mostly common and benign, they also tended to exist as mutualists in some environments.

For those readers who might not be scientifically inclined, that just means the two bacteria can work together for the benefit of both. Specifically, it had been noticed decades ago that Streptococcus and Veillonella could exist together in the human digestive tract. Living in tandem, as neighbors, one grows with sugar and releases lactic acid as waste, the other uses the waste as energy and discards short-chain fatty acids that are less acidic than lactic acid. That term of short chain fatty acids immediately caught my eye.

My previous research into intestinal biomes had taught me that bacteria living in the gut tended to digest fiber as energy. Because of chemical processes that have to do with a lack of oxygen in such environments, they tend to release short-chain fatty acid as a final product. That, in turn, could be used by some human cells for energy. Short-chain fatty acid was also known to have medicinal properties in Eastern and homeopathic forms of medicine. Even today apple cider vinegar, itself a form of short-chain fatty acid, is advised as a treatment for all kinds of ailments.

The concept of short-chain fatty acid as a key part of the human biome also aligned with my own experience as a child in Hanlou. Like many villagers, my family would often eat meals made up of dried vegetables and no meat. Such a diet could provide a person with plenty of energy and lead to health and vitality.

As I continued my research online, I found many scientists suspected that short-chain fatty acids could calm the intestinal immune system. Some had even demonstrated that such reactions were possible in a petri dish. Why couldn't the same dynamic work in the oral microbiome?

Suddenly, I had the missing link that tied my version of the hygiene hypothesis together.

Streptococcus and Veillonella have evolved alongside primates like us for millions of years. Our bodies are their natural homes. And we, in turn, have gotten quite used to having them around. So much so that they perform valuable roles, helping us break down sugars and lactic acid to regulate our immune systems. Modern oral hygiene has suppressed both, leading to allergic reactions. We could no longer tolerate everyday substances like pollen because we didn't have the natural peacemakers we could rely upon.

Oral probiotic deficiency caused my allergies. It was a good theory. But could I prove it?

Designing a New Allergy Remedy

THE USUAL WAY TO test a hypothesis like the one I was proposing would be to gather hundreds, possibly thousands, of people and study their oral microbiomes for a long time. Ideally, some of them would see their allergies go away, at which point it would be possible to conduct the kind of before-and-after analysis I had done myself.

Such a study would be worthwhile, but it would cost a fortune – I estimated the expenses would run well into the hundreds of thousands. In fact, it might take *millions*. On top of that you have to find volunteers who would consent to share saliva samples for years on end. Even worse, you'd be banking on the somewhat unlikely coincidence that a statistically significant number of them would lose their allergic symptoms in that time. What had happened to me was a short-lived rarity; expecting it in dozens or hundreds of cases would be difficult. I had already had my grant applications denied for projects that were much more straightforward. Who was going to fund a study like the one I had in mind?

With all of this in mind, I decided (once again) to abandon a broad approach and go deeper. If I felt like I had identified the cause of my allergic symptoms, then the question in front of me was whether or not I could reverse the process and, rather than studying thousands of people, I could try to do something different for myself and then see if the results could be replicated. Doing so would not cost nearly as much, and I would only need my own permission.

That's not to say there were no risks involved. Although I certainly had the resources I needed to conduct another small experiment, the idea I had was new. Nothing in my research had suggested that anyone had attempted to alter an individual's microbiome in such a targeted way before. It was entirely possible that I would fail once again.

I knew I had to at least put my idea to the test. I felt certain that modern oral hygiene habits were exacerbating allergy symptoms. And, I thought I understood which bacteria were needed to pacify the immune system. What I *didn't* know was how I could use that information to help others.

If my situation were typical, then most allergy sufferers weren't missing the two types of bacteria that would pacify their immune systems, they just didn't have enough of them. Luckily, microorganisms replenish themselves very quickly, dividing two to three times every hour under the right conditions. Knowing this, I started asking myself: what do Strepto-coccus and Veillonella like to eat? And how could I give it to them? If I could figure out how to bring them back, then perhaps the balance could be restored.

Luckily, this was an area with lots of established science behind it. In the 50 or 60 years of research that went into Strep-tococcus and Veillonella, researchers had determined they could be nourished with six or seven sugars, along with some key amino acids. All the ingredients were common enough that I could find them either online or at a local store. So, I started adding them together in my kitchen, making notes of the different proportions and the tastes and textures that came from each combination.

The first few batches were less than inspiring. I had been aiming for a kind of candy but came away with a sickly sweet fudge that didn't have a particularly appetizing look or smell. Still, I would take a deep breath, tell myself it was for science, and take a bite.

My technique improved with practice. It was my first time cooking with sugars and I enjoyed the process. It reminded me of my days as a bachelor, as well as the various hands-on lab experiments I had done as a student. Eventually, I got creative and started adding new ingredients like almonds to help with the form and taste. If I were going to make a homemade prebi-otic, then it just stood to reason that it should be as palatable as possible.

It was that spring, in March of 2017, when my seasonal aller-gies came back with a vengeance. I knew it was time to put my theories to work. Using what I'd learned, I created the first AllerPops prototypes and consumed them myself.

The results were mixed. On the one hand, I *was* getting allergy relief. In fact, my symptoms would nearly disappear for several hours at a time, making my prototypes more effective than any drug I had tried. On the other hand, that relief would only last for a few hours. In order to keep the sneezing at bay I had to eat three or four of my early AllerPops every day. Not only did that mean keeping them around almost constantly, but I worried what all that sugar would do to my teeth and body. There was a certain irony in blaming dental care for my allergies while simultaneously wondering if I was giving myself cavities from eating sugar to fight the allergies.

The bigger issue was that the short-lived effectiveness of my treatments went against my theories. By my own estimations, the new bacteria in my mouth should have lived for at least a couple of days. I couldn't figure out why I was needing to encourage growth so frequently.

I didn't get much of a chance to go looking for answers. One Sunday afternoon I went out into my backyard intending to do some work on our garden. After just a few minutes I realized I felt chilly, and perhaps a bit tired. Remembering that Kathy had recently gone through some sort of illness, I wondered if it had caught up to me. The thermometer showed I had a slight fever, with my temperature being just a few degrees higher than it should be.

I decided to take the day off from yard work. I also stopped eating my AllerPops prototypes, deciding it wouldn't be a good idea to promote bacteria growth in my body at the same time I was fighting an infection.

Given that my symptoms were mild, I opted not to take any medication for my fever. This decision didn't have anything to do with my allergies or research, but I believe it paid big dividends later and helped me move unintentionally towards my understanding of the oral microbiome. Destiny was prodding me yet again.

The fever was still with me on Monday morning. I decided to stay home and rest for a speedy recovery. While preparing to sleep in the evening I happened to look at my tongue in the mirror. It was completely red. That made sense, given that I had a higher than normal temperature. I had seen the same in medical patients battling various infections for years; there wasn't anything unusual about it.

On this particular occasion, though, the color of my tongue gave me a new inspiration. At that moment it occurred to me that my mouth, red and inflamed as it was, was like a field that had just gone through a wildfire. As any farmer could tell you, that's the best time to plant a new crop – the ground is empty and packed with nutrition.

Suddenly I understood that I hadn't been handling my test correctly. If I wanted to grow new bacteria I needed to wait for an environment when my microbiome was as clear as possible. I had to plant after the wildfire. My fever was a gift. It was going to allow me to grow good bacteria in a fresh field.

I waited until Tuesday afternoon when my fever had broken. When I was sure the worst of it had passed I took two AllerPops prototypes and then went back to bed. There wasn't any way to be sure what would happen, but I felt strongly that my instincts were correct. I was working with hope and intuition first, hoping the observational data would back me up later.

My optimism was rewarded. In fact, my samples worked better than expected under the new conditions. When I woke up on Wednesday morning my allergy symptoms were completely gone. It was amazing. All at once I felt clear, with breath coming to me easily. My nose wasn't stuffy, my eyes didn't water, and I hadn't experienced any trouble sleeping through the night.

That's when it dawned on me that I might have invented something that was safe, affordable, and (most importantly) effective at reducing allergy symptoms for more than a few hours. If I could make it available to others it would change the lives of millions of people around the world. My head was swimming with different questions, ideas, and possibilities.

The next day I met my lawyer and friend, James Kennedy III, in the biggest park in Los Alamos. It was March 15, 2017, right at the peak of juniper pollen season, and I felt nothing except joy for the lovely spring day. It was a situation that would have seemed impossible only a week before.

Ironically, we were getting together to discuss a patent for my Knoze wet mask product. By then I realized I might have something bigger to talk with him about. This time traveler was about to become a full-fledged entrepreneur.

7

LAUNCHING ALLERPOPS

I t is often said that starting your own company is part of the American dream. That might be true. But I can also tell you that risking your money, reputation, and future on an unproven concept is as terrifying as it is exhilarating.

I had dabbled in entrepreneurship before starting Aller-Pops, but after my prototype test I didn't want to spend just a few hours each week trying to make extra money anymore. This time I was starting my company for real.

I had learned a lot from the wet mask endeavor, but sales were coming slowly and it was hard to scale the idea. Sewing masks at home in my spare time had been an interesting experience, but it was time to think bigger.

Looking back, perhaps I should have been daunted by the challenge in front of me. At the time, though, I felt like I had everything I needed for success. I knew my product and idea were sound. I had a desire to offer customers something safe and life-changing for a relatively small amount of money. And, at the bottom of my heart, I knew I would not die peacefully without trying it.

This time I would need to go all in on my inspiration. That

would mean refining my product even further. It would also mean working with lawyers, accountants, and marketing professionals to get the details right. If I were ever going to see the day when AllerPops was a real venture, I'd have to work through late hours while becoming a better entrepreneur. I'd need to turn my persistent nature onto the study of business.

I felt fully prepared to make those sacrifices and take on the challenge. Not only would success mean altering the course of my own career, but also improving things for my family *and* millions of allergy sufferers around the world.

I had the sense that all my life had been leading up to that point. Everything I wanted was right in front of me. But before I could get it, I would need to make the most important sale of my life: I would have to convince my wife, Kathy, that the risks we would be taking together would be worth it.

TURNING Destiny Into Reality

I'm sure any married entrepreneur will remember the moment when they had to explain the desire to start a new company to their spouse. It's hard enough to give up a steady paycheck when you're putting your own life at risk. To do it when you have a partner and children to support is something entirely different.

I should also remind my readers that I was in my early 50s at this point. My wife and I had both worked incredibly hard to make it to our comfortable, financially secure position. We had reached a point where a lot of people might be reasonably thinking about how they would wind down their careers and retire in style. Instead, I wanted to give up my generous government salary and place it all on the roulette wheel of entrepreneurship.

Needless to say, our initial conversation didn't go that well.

Kathy was concerned and upset that I wanted to trade our stability for the chance at something bigger. It wasn't that she didn't trust me or have a desire to support my dreams; it was simply the case that she is a smart and informed woman. She was well aware that 95% of all new business ventures will eventually fail. Like me, she had lived in a time and place where most people didn't have much and wanted to provide a better life for her children.

I couldn't disagree with any of that, but I did offer a few counter arguments. First, I pointed out that I could take an early retirement from the Department of Energy. My pension would be much smaller than my regular salary, of course, but it would still be enough to support the family while I looked for work if AllerPops failed. I also reminded her that since my reassignment away from the Human Genome Project, I was spending my days on projects that weren't a great match for my skills and ambitions.

But most of all, I told her that life had put me in a position to work on something that could bring relief to millions of people. I could feel in my heart that the AllerPops concept was new, different, and beneficial. It was going to offer a glimpse of hope for people like myself who had gotten used to living without it. There were children out there, just like our son, who could live in a world where allergies couldn't keep them from enjoying the same things everyone else took for granted.

As our conversations became more serious the decision seemed to take on a life of its own. Giving up my job would have meant taking away two-thirds of our income. And, it would have meant doing it at a time when we still had a mortgage to pay and two kids nearing college.

Even my daughter felt the tension. When she found out what I was considering she wrote me a sort of essay outlining all the reasons I should maintain my current career path, followed by a list of entrepreneurs who had found success while holding a day job. I had to admire her persistence and research skills as an eighth grader.

I also had to admit that both my wife and my daughter were making good points. It was true that sinking our life savings into something that wasn't guaranteed to work out brought enormous dangers. But to me the bigger risk was passing up on the opportunity to do something special. I didn't want to live the rest of my life knowing that the chance to leave my mark and become the best version of myself had gotten away.

It took some time, but Kathy eventually compromised with me. I would take a temporary leave from my position at the Department of Energy and see how things went from there.

I love her for supporting me on something she was clearly skeptical about. I know she was nervous about the decision, but she was also willing to believe in me and share my hope. She even took a bit of her own personal savings and put it towards my starting capital!

With Kathy's blessing in place, I had the green light to jump into the details and bring AllerPops to life. I met with an attorney and repeated the patent process again. Then, I informed my team at the Department of Energy that I would be taking an extended break. And finally, I started exploring the details involved with incorporation, branding, production, and financing.

The excitement and fear were turned up several notches. It dawned on me that my journey to becoming a full-time entrepreneur was moving forward. This thing I had dreamed about was *actually happening*.

A Recipe for Growth

Although there are dozens of details involved, the truth is the paperwork aspects of starting a company aren't so difficult if you have a bit of time and money, along with the right team of advisors. What was more pressing to me was ensuring I had a business model that could sustain faster growth later.

In order to build a company that would be profitable I had to come up with three things: a repeatable production process, a proof of my concept, and more money to work with.

Without the right production process – a recipe for Aller-Pops that could be followed again and again – the other two wouldn't matter. So I began there.

My early attempts at home baking prototypes had been hit-or-miss. I hardly had any recipe at all. It certainly wasn't something a bigger manufacturing plant would be able to follow. In addition, some of the early attempts left me with a concoction that was sticky, fuzzy, and didn't have much shelf life. I needed to come up with a formula that would taste better, hold up when shipped or mailed, and be duplicated again and again.

Naturally I gathered a team of scientists, bakers, and biological engineers who could help me generate the right molecular formula as a hard gel substance. We spent months in labs and test kitchens, burning through millions of dollars of ingredients.

I'm kidding. I didn't have the money or connections for a process like that. Instead, I turned to Google and YouTube. I knew that, chemically speaking, what I was inventing was a kind of therapeutic candy. So, I looked up videos and tutorials on the basics of confectionery baking. I simply learned to make hard candy at home and then substituted in the ingredients I needed to promote the growth of good bacteria.

Every day I made several batches of homemade hard candy,

to the point that my wife and kids got sick of trying them. After generating so many batches that I was filling our trash bins with uneaten candy, I started using my brain more creatively. I bought a set of small steel measuring cups and started using them to bake tiny candies.

It took a few weeks of experimentation. But eventually I came up with a recipe that had a great taste and could be reliably duplicated using common ingredients.

Or at least that's what I thought. I knew that the most cost-effective manufacturing in the world can be found in China. Luckily, I happened to speak the language. I reached out to a few different plants as I was testing new recipes. Eventually, I settled on a provider I was sure I could trust to keep quality standards high.

Even then it took several rounds of back-and-forth testing and communication to get things right. Inevitably they used ingredients and coatings that were slightly different from mine. It was a tedious process, but I was committed to having my product as tasty and consistent as it possibly could be.

Fortunately, they were patient with me and offered their own suggestions. Before long we came up with a product that seemed to match my vision perfectly. The most important technical challenge was out of the way.

As I was refining the product, I also wanted to provide a process that would make it work for customers. You might recall that my own breakthrough with the AllerPops prototypes had come after my fever. To me, that was a gift from God that led to the last missing piece of the puzzle. If you don't like that explanation, you could just call it the kind of happy accident that makes scientific progress possible.

Either way, I had learned that it's best to start with a clean slate when trying to build up the good bacteria in your mouth and throat. How, I wondered, could I create those same conditions for others?

My first thought was to encourage a natural approach. In the weeks after my allergies subsided I noticed that my son hadn't seen the same improvement. He was using AllerPops prototypes, but only getting a few hours of relief with each dose. I wondered whether it wouldn't have been better for him if he had gotten sick when I did. After all, the body has its own healing processes. Our job is often to just encourage them. There was probably nothing I could think of that would be as effective as a natural fever for clearing his biome as it had mine.

As tempting as the idea was, I decided it wasn't practical. I certainly didn't want my son to be sick if he didn't need to be. And looking ahead, telling people to seek out a virus didn't seem like a sustainable (or marketable) way to promote an allergy treatment. Even if the fever were introduced artificially it seemed as if the risks and complications were just too great. The fever solution was off the table.

After a few days another idea arrived. What about trying to heat the area locally? I was aware that some cancer treatments involved heating certain parts of the body to kill the deadly cells within. Could that be accomplished in a less dramatic way to clear the mouth of existing bacteria and let favored varieties grow? I couldn't see why not.

I started testing the concept, beginning with myself. I soon learned that rinsing the mouth out with hot water, and a bit of regular brushing, was enough for most people to see improvement. It might not be as beneficial as a natural fever, but it would give the average allergy sufferer longer-lasting relief from their symptoms.

With that I had the product and process I needed to help millions of people. I just needed a space to contain my growing enterprise.

· · ·

GETTING Out of the House

Somewhere between baking my hundredth batch of candy and meeting with a lawyer for the tenth or twentieth time I came to an obvious conclusion: I would need to move the business out of my house to keep growing.

Because I was still responsible for every aspect of the growing company – from writing the text on the packaging to tweaking the recipes – I wanted a short commute. But at the same time I needed space to store inventory, make video calls, and (perhaps most importantly) give my family a break from the long hours I was putting into the project.

After some searching online, I found a space in Los Alamos that would fit perfectly. It had enough parking to handle delivery trucks, a large space that could be used for research and storage, and even a small office where I could run my company. The only issue was that it was completely bare.

I wasn't about to waste money that could go towards growing my company, so the first thing I did was create all the necessary furniture myself. It's not an exaggeration to say I built it all from scratch. It took me back to my days as a graduate student in China, when my advisor and I had to put together the shelves and equipment we needed to carry out experiments.

Over the course of a few weeks in 2018 I transformed my business space into exactly what I needed. I began the process by ripping out the existing carpet. Then, I constructed five different 4' x 8' book racks that could hold the inventory I kept on hand. Next I built a storage cabinet, along with several shelves.

Manual labor is never glamorous, and sawing boards might not fit with the glorified image many people have of entrepreneurship. But I was thrilled to have my own space and the freedom to launch my company on my own terms. To this day I feel a sense of pride and commitment when I look around and see the facility I've built with my own hands, stocked with products I designed and tested myself.

How strongly can you really believe in any dream if you aren't willing to get your hands dirty to achieve it?

When I was done building I had everything I needed, and the first shipment of my product was on the way. Now I had to prove it would work and get the word out. The real work was about to begin.

8

REACHING OUT TO THE WORLD

The first production batch of my allergy reduction lollipops arrived in January 2018. That day came to me with a combination of exhilaration and unease. I was about to see my dream turned into a reality while possibly introducing millions to a safe, affordable, and effective treatment for their symptoms. But I was also giving up 21 years of steady employment on a risky endeavor. It's a wonderful and terrifying thing to bet your family's future on *any* idea, no matter how sure you are about it.

I felt certain that my allergy treatment would work. But as a doctor and researcher I knew I didn't have enough verification to be sure. There were all kinds of things that could theoretically go wrong. Even though I was using tested ingredients to follow a scientifically sound concept, you could never be sure how different people's bodies – not to mention the buying public – would react.

In this way, I feel like my journey as an entrepreneur has been an act of faith. It takes an interesting blend of optimism and naivety to start a company. I was facing that reality when those first boxes arrived. I simply had to trust in my God, myself, and my destiny. Circumstances, and a sense of persistence, had put me in a unique position. All that was left was to see things through.

With that mindset I decided to start selling my product.

Early Sales and Reviews

There are probably dozens of ways to launch a product, and I certainly investigated numerous books and reviews on the topic. In the end, though, I opted for the most straightforward approach I could think of: seeing if I could get friends and colleagues to purchase a few as a starting point.

The conventional wisdom would have suggested that I should have given away hundreds or thousands of free samples. I considered that, but decided against it for a couple of reasons. First, I don't particularly like or value free products myself. I know that more often than not they tend to find their way into a garbage can without ever being used. I didn't want people discarding my allergy solution for the wrong reasons.

The second reason had to do with the product itself. As I had experimented with my prototypes and allergy treatment, I learned that my solution worked best under certain conditions. For instance, users had to gargle with warm water and reduce their dental hygiene activities for a few days if they wanted good bacteria to grow. If someone didn't follow those instructions, then there was a low probability they would receive any benefit.

By giving away free samples I would have been offering my products to people who might not actually care that much about using them the right way. That, in turn, could have made them less effective. Then, the early reviews might have led me to the wrong conclusions or caused my new company to acquire a bad reputation. I wanted to find users like myself who were bothered enough by their allergies to take the process seriously. They were the ones I was sure I could help.

That meant growing my initial customer base slowly and organically. However, it also meant that the people who *did* use the first AllerPops were willing to give them an honest try and then share their feedback. It took some time, but I eventually started to learn a few things from their reports.

The first, to my great relief, was that my products were actually working. Dozens of early customers came back to report that their allergy symptoms were subsiding. Some of them were getting relief they hadn't found for years, or even decades. That was fantastic news, and it gave me the encouragement I needed to keep offering them to more people.

Not everything was perfect, however. For one thing, those early customers were using my lollipops in different ways. Some were buying my product and letting it sit for weeks or months without giving it a try. When I made inquiries I learned that the detailed instructions made it hard for them to get started. My scientific mind was thinking about maximum effect where my business mind should have been focused on making the process as simple as possible. The realization led me to simplify the steps and become better attuned to my customers.

More troubling was the fact that a handful of people were experiencing side effects, mostly fatigue, mild headaches, and possibly a light fever. This was new information for me. I couldn't understand why the simple recipe I had put together would cause anyone problems. The ingredients were all known and proven; there shouldn't have been any issues. Still, there was obviously *something* going on. I could have ignored one or two reports as being coincidental (for instance, someone picking up an unrelated infection while starting use of my products). However, even though there weren't many complaints, they were consistent enough that I had to consider the cause.

It took some time to figure things out, but I eventually got to the root of the problem: when the user would eat too many AllerPops, the effect could come on too quickly and strongly. With the good bacteria in their mouth and throat going from a low concentration to a high concentration in a short amount of time, the immune system would find itself relaxing all at once. It was the body's equivalent of shifting rapidly into a lower gear. The user might have tissue that had been damaged from sneezing, for example, or prolonged inflammation. Now, the product was inviting an overload of bacteria to come in and do more damage. That expressed itself through tiredness, headaches, and higher temperatures.

That realization allowed me to improve the instructions and recommendations I provided new customers. It also made me realize that I had to simplify the directions I was providing to users who weren't as familiar with science as I was. Although the first version of my product came with 17 different steps, customers today only have to follow a few simple guidelines. Thankfully, the benefits of using AllerPops have remained while reported side effects are extraordinarily rare.

When I think back to this time I can still remember the excitement that came with launching my own company. Even more than that, however, I'm extraordinarily grateful to the people who put their trust in me, bought my early products, and took the time to help me refine them. If you're one of those individuals, know that my company couldn't have grown without your help and I'm grateful to you every day.

MOVING to the Next Level

As the boxes in my makeshift warehouse started to empty, with products being shipped to customers around Los Alamos and beyond, it became obvious that I would need to leave the Department of Energy permanently. There just wasn't enough time in the day. Even though people tell you that being an entrepreneur is busy work, I never expected I would wear so many hats.

On any given morning I might have been my company's product researcher, production manager, and chief marketing officer for short stretches. Later I could have served as the mail room attendant, receptionist, and janitor. I also did some light accounting, all while keeping my original job as the on-staff carpenter.

I quickly realized that I needed all of my day just to stay on top of the essential tasks. Then I came to understand that my own time and expertise weren't enough. I needed help. More than that, I needed advice and perspectives from people who knew more than I did.

My local Small Business Administration branch put me in touch with a handful of Service Corps of Retired Executives (or SCORE) mentors who gave me invaluable advice. In particular, Lee Lefton, Jim Owens, and Russ Mooney all provided insights that I just wasn't able to reach on my own.

For example, up until that point I had been calling my product *Knoze Jr. Prebiotic Lollipops*. As a former copywriter, Lee gently pointed out that my complicated name wasn't helping anyone understand what it was or how it would benefit them. Few people picked up on the notion that *Knoze* referred to *nose*, and the rest was just too long. After batting around some potential replacements, including the fun and descriptive *Aller Terminator*, he helped me settle on AllerPops.

Together, the three of them helped me refine not only my

business plan, but my vision for the company. In the process they probably shaved years off my learning curve as an entrepreneur.

Another who helped me with his time and experience was Joe Montes. As director of the Small Business Development Council (or SBDC) in Los Alamos, he had seen lots of entrepreneurs come and go. He had similar criticisms of my early product name and packaging. He especially disliked that the boxes made it seem as if I were selling a kind of candy.

I explained to him that I had been worried about running afoul of FDA regulations, which gives lots of guidelines about what you can and cannot say regarding the therapeutic value of a product like mine. Joe was understanding, but still insisted that I needed to beef up my marketing. Then he gave me a piece of advice that changed my perspective. He simply told me that the regulations were important boundaries, but that as an entrepreneur it was my job to explore the area within those boundaries.

My mentor went on to explain that many industry guidelines are written by lawyers who work for the biggest firms. They weren't necessarily there to protect consumers but instead to limit competition. He told me I shouldn't ever break these rules, but also not to forget that I had to ask myself how I could operate within them if I wanted to stay in business.

These are only some short examples of the great advice I got from these early mentors. By spending time with them I was able to sharpen my business plan and improve my marketing. Although I eventually had to find my own team of paid staff (consisting of an attorney, an accountant, a marketing launch coordinator, and so on), I'll never forget the advice I got from those men. I look forward to the day when I am successful enough as an entrepreneur to pass along what I've learned to someone new.

That wasn't my biggest concern at the time, however. I was

more focused on sharing AllerPops with an audience that was much bigger than my extended social circle.

A Fair Chance of Success

The AllerPops patent application was fast-tracked, with our first patent issued late in 2017. The following months kept me busy with more market testing, along with the dozens of tasks needed to get a new business moving. I needed to put up a website, design brochures, and even think ahead to bigger product launches. Before all of that, though, I wanted some more direct feedback from buyers.

In September of 2019, my wife and I ventured to the New Mexico State Fair. The plan was to offer AllerPops directly to the public over the course of nine days. It seemed like the perfect opportunity to test out different marketing pitches and get some instant feedback on my product. We bought a booth in a busy area with lots of foot traffic and prepared for the inevitable rush of new customers who would be interested in a safe and effective non-prescription allergy treatment.

Nothing would make me happier than telling you how we sold out of our existing inventory on the first day. Unfortunately, that's not exactly what happened. Not only were we struggling to attract buyers, but most people didn't even stop to talk. They simply shuffled by, glanced in our direction, and then resumed their path to whatever concert, spectacle, or corn dog stand they had set out to find.

It might've been easier to deal with if everyone were having the same problems, but that clearly wasn't the case. Across from us was another booth selling makeup products. It was manned by a youngish man, probably in his 20s, who always seemed to be surrounded by a crowd. I wondered what he was doing that Kathy and I weren't.

By the third day I got desperate enough to start wearing a white Einstein wig and glasses. My reasoning was that if people would at least notice our booth, then they might pay attention to what we were offering. It didn't work, at least in terms of helping us generate sales. However, it did have another effect: our sales-savvy neighbor finally took pity on us and offered some coaching.

His name was Nathan Usupov, and he had learned about business the hard way after immigrating from Israel years before we met him. Nathan patiently explained to Kathy and me that we couldn't simply wait for traffic to come to our booth. We had to go out and be with the people, engaging them, before they would take an interest in our product. Another neighbor, Omar Barreto, recommended I lose the wig. I wanted attention, of course, but also to be taken seriously.

Stepping into the crowd and talking to strangers was painfully awkward, particularly for someone as shy as myself. After a day or two, though, it started to feel natural. It even got to be a little bit fun. I discovered that I loved talking about AllerPops and the story behind my company. Sales started coming in slowly, at first, and then more quickly.

Once we finally started moving boxes filled with inventory out of the booth it was time to begin testing different pricing strategies. I would offer boxes of a dozen AllerPops for $40 on one day and then $30 for the next, comparing the results.

From this exercise I learned a pair of truths. The first was that the specific price didn't make any difference for some people. If they needed allergy relief and were intrigued by the idea, then the cost wasn't a major consideration. The second, however, was that for some of my customers, choosing to try my product meant skipping out on some little luxury (like lunch at the fair) that they had budgeted for. This touched me. Obviously, I want my company to be financially successful, but I also want to provide a convenient and affordable form of relief to those who need it most. Having met those customers face to face, I decided to make AllerPops as affordable as possible – both at the fair and in the future.

While visiting the state fair didn't make us rich, I do think it was an incredibly important step on my journey as an entrepreneur. Just as there isn't any substitute for working on your business with your own hands, neither can you duplicate the experience of meeting buyers face to face. The better you know them, the easier it is to change their lives for the better. That's where the real profits are.

I'm glad I learned those lessons when I did. It helped prepare me for the next step. It was time to raise the money needed to introduce my product to the world.

Reaching Out to the Public

Some people like to say that timing is everything. I'm not sure I agree. To me, persistence is the key to success in any field or effort. But I have to admit that it's much easier to move forward with your dream when the conditions are stacked in your favor.

You might remember that I was first able to earn my PhD because of a strange set of circumstances that were occurring in China at the time. As people were flocking into the country's growing private sector, it created openings in the academic world that weren't there before. Likewise, I met my wife online at a time when those sort of introductions were new. Had we been inundated with apps where millions of people were swiping left and right, maybe we wouldn't have taken the time to get to know each other.

In a sense, I feel like the same thing happened when I went searching for ways to fund my growing business. At a different time or place, trying to find funding for my growing company would have meant sitting in boardrooms or filing endless proposals. As it was, however, I was able to take my pitch directly to the public through the magic of crowdfunding.

After joining the platform Wefunder, I made a series of simple videos explaining my background and unique approach to allergy relief. I used plain language to explain how prebiotics work, adding that I had been able to alleviate my own symptoms almost completely – and keep the sneezing away – with my product.

This straightforward appeal struck a chord with individual investors, to the point that they put more than a quarter of a million dollars into AllerPops. Now I had the capital I needed to start offering my creation to the public. I brought in talented people to help me with marketing and finance.

As the crowdfunding effort was unfolding, I promoted AllerPops online and met with local retailers. I didn't have enormous budgets, of course, so progress was slow and incremental those first couple of years. Soon, though, word started to spread around my part of New Mexico that there was a new treatment for allergy symptoms.

Precise numbers are hard to come by, but we estimate that somewhere between 5,000 and 10,000 people were using AllerPops by 2021. Even better, they were telling us about the benefits. Customers started saying they felt better than they had in years, and that their allergy symptoms weren't coming back for months. Best of all, when their symptoms *did* return, they were able to reset their immune systems with another dose of their favorite tasty treat.

Things were going beautifully. There was nothing to do but move into the next phase of the company's growth. That meant more crowdfunding. I also began to look for angel investors who could contribute cash and expertise to the business, helping turn it into a well-known product.

Bringing AllerPops to the World

One of the most difficult things about telling your story in a book is the need to condense facts and details into paragraphs of chapters that move along. There isn't room for discussion of each long meeting, sleepless night, or difficult decision. I can't talk enough about the dozens of hours spent researching, analyzing data, or even just trying to find the right color or sweetness for my product prototype.

Given that reality, I hope you'll understand it's an understatement to say it has taken a tremendous amount of effort, by myself, my family, and all the people who helped me, to get AllerPops off the ground and functioning as a business. But at the point that I'm writing this, in Autumn of 2021, I can see that things are finally falling into place.

My new company has a great product. We raised a substantial amount of money through an initial crowdfunding effort and found a base of customers who love what we make. FDA approval is right around the corner, and the business is ready to take the next leap forward.

As I work through these chapters my team and I are making plans for the next phase of growth. Some of that will be driven by angel investors who have both the capital and know-how we need to expand into more markets. It's possible there will be another round of crowdfunding, or even multiple opportunities for small investors to get involved. Although it isn't exactly clear what form that growth in funding will take, I can tell it's time.

Part of me is still amazed that AllerPops exist at all. If you could go back in time with me and see the shy, stubborn child I was, you would understand. I don't think anyone would have imagined that boy as an entrepreneur, and certainly not someone who could meet with reporters and investors to tell them about his company.

I credit much of this transformation to the faith and confidence God has instilled within me. Opening up the spiritual dimension of my life hasn't only brought me peace and joy, but also a sense of belonging that wasn't there before. It gave me the confidence to become the best version of myself.

My other inspiration is the mission and destiny that have been given to me. I want to change the world for allergy sufferers, and truly believe everything that happened in my life led me to that point and purpose. So, whenever I feel like I can't do something, or there is just too much work remaining, I remember that I'm simply doing the thing I was meant for. It's all part of the process, and the context always matters.

All of that is made easier by the fact that AllerPops products are bringing relief to people who couldn't find it before. That brings me more pride and joy than any other accomplishment. As much as I would love to tell you about the wonderful benefits of my creation, it's better if you hear the success stories firsthand.

9

ALLERPOPS CUSTOMERS IN THEIR OWN WORDS

Although necessity has dictated I spend the majority of this book telling you about my background and the circumstances that led to the creation of Aller-Pops, the best part of the story has nothing to do with me. That's because my proudest moments as a scientist and entrepreneur have come from seeing the way someone else's life can be changed by a product or process I invented.

That being the case, I wanted to include a section in this book where people who used to suffer from allergies could tell their own stories. After all, it's one thing to hear about a new twist on the hygiene hypothesis from me; it's another thing to read the impressions of real people in their own words.

I have gathered some stories from actual AllerPops customers who agreed to be interviewed for this book. Here's what they had to say...

"I'm Free to Enjoy the Outdoors Just Like Everyone Else"

I had always been affected by light allergies, but I didn't really pay much attention to them until I moved from

Minnesota to New Mexico almost 40 years ago. Suddenly *everything* seemed to get me. From cats to hay fever and pine pollen, there wasn't much that wouldn't make me sneeze.

Entire parts of the year were ruined. From February to March juniper would be in the air and my head would be so congested I couldn't breathe. From August until November or December, hay and wheat would send me into sneezing fits. Even with neti pots, allergy sprays, and stronger medications I couldn't approach anything close to a normal life. It wasn't just affecting me; my poor husband had to suffer through my snoring, asthma, and bad moods.

What made it worse was feeling like a prisoner. While my family and friends went to see baseball games, rodeos, and other outdoor events, I had to stay away. On some occasions I might try to medicate myself heavily, but that would just lead to an asthmatic reaction – I could suffer one way or another, but not actually enjoy the warm weather with everyone else.

Like most people with allergies, I tried everything I could think of and then gave up when nothing seemed to work. It felt as if my symptoms were just going to be a permanent part of my life.

I was lucky enough to know Dr. Han socially for many years when he began his company. I was aware of his background but hadn't given it a great deal of thought until he launched his first crowdfunding campaign. When I saw his videos and research put together for the public I realized just how much work he had put into the project. I figured I owed it to him, and myself, to give AllerPops a try.

I think I used four pops in that first cycle. It didn't seem like such a small step could change anything, particularly given that I had been trying to fight my allergy symptoms for years. But then, in less than a week, my sneezing, congestion, and watery eyes were *just gone*. I couldn't believe it.

The sneezing and symptoms that had tormented me for

years just disappeared. Even better, they stayed away. It's been more than two years since I have been affected.

With time, I've adjusted my oral hygiene habits a bit. Sometimes I brush my teeth only with water. And I am a bit more conscious about not over-cleaning or sanitizing my mouth. I'm certainly not an expert in the science, but experience has taught me that these steps might be as important as the pops themselves.

It's hard to believe the solution to my allergy problems could have been so simple. Not only have I continued using AllerPops, but I've become very proactive about introducing my friends to the product. I've gotten four or five to try them already. Instead of getting into the research, I just have them follow the instructions precisely. The response is always the same: people are amazed at how well they work.

I no longer have allergy symptoms. I'm free to enjoy the outside world with my friends and family just like everyone else. It would be hard for me to say enough about what Dr. Han's product means to me, or the many ways it has changed my life. So, I'll just say that I hope more people keep trying it and enjoying the same results I have.

Karen
Pueblo, Colorado

...

"I've Been Liberated From a Lifetime of Allergy Symptoms"

I've suffered from allergies for as long as I can remember. I mean that literally. When I was a four- or five-year-old child, my father used to tell me to stop sniffing constantly. This was despite the fact that he was always sneezing, and that his eyes were usually watery. My mother was also allergic to everything in sight, from cats and dogs to certain soaps and perfumes.

Throughout my life the symptoms became a more and more prevalent distraction. I was always very interested in sports but struggled to compete because my watery eyes and stuffy nose held me back. Things got even worse when I moved from the Midwest to California. My regular congestion became more severe and I started suffering from eczema and migraine headaches, as well.

The worst part about the suffering was that I didn't even know where it came from. Eventually I dated a nurse who noticed my pain and suggested I was probably allergic to many different things. Armed with that knowledge I started taking all kinds of medications – including the name brands every allergy sufferer has tried. They helped for short periods of time, but the relief was never lasting. Also, the side effects were sometimes worse than the symptoms themselves.

I didn't like having allergies, but I also knew I couldn't keep taking big doses of powerful medicines forever. It wasn't a good situation for my health *or* my sanity.

One day I saw a commercial for AllerPops while watching television. Anything having to do with allergies caught my eye, so I wrote down the website address that was shown and started reading through the background information. I decided to call the company and, to my great surprise, Dr. Han answered the phone himself. He was happy to walk me through his research and process.

Even after the rationale for AllerPops was explained to me I couldn't see how it would work for anyone, and certainly not for a person with my symptoms. It wasn't that the science seemed off. Instead, I figured that if Dr. Han's treatment for allergies was actually as effective as he seemed to think, I would have already heard about it. Still, I was desperate so I ordered a box.

When my first batch of AllerPops arrived I called Dr. Han again to confirm the instructions for use. I figured that if I was going to try the product I might as well do it the right way.

I ended up going through several cycles of AllerPops. I didn't expect much, but I had already paid for them so I figured, "Why not?" It was during the third cycle that I began noticing changes. I was a bit less congested before and could sleep again. By the fifth cycle my allergy symptoms had completely disappeared. It was an actual, real-life miracle. I was so floored by the change that I called Dr. Han once more. I wanted him to know how amazing his product was, and to offer to drive down to Los Alamos and take him out to lunch.

In the three years since I started using AllerPops I've not had another migraine. In fact, my allergy symptoms only returned once – after I took antibiotics to deal with kidney stones. And even then I was able to get back to normal life after a couple cycles of fresh pops.

I never would have imagined that such a simple solution would change everything for me. But what can I say? AllerPops just work. They have literally liberated me from my symptoms, not to mention half a dozen different medications.

Dr. Han's product and attention have far, far exceeded any of my expectations. I'm so grateful to have found them and will happily recommend them to any allergy sufferer... and especially someone with as many issues as I've had. Relief is closer than you think!

Martin
Santa Fe, New Mexico

...

"It's Like Night and Day"

My fight with allergies goes all the way back to the 1970s. I can still remember my first reaction. The constant coughing, runny nose, and miserable feeling hung over me for weeks after I had moved from California to Iowa.

Later in life I moved again, this time to New Mexico. The allergic sensitivity came with me. Juniper season tended to be the worst. Certain medications helped a little, but even then doctors warned that prolonged use wasn't good for your heart. And they didn't do a great deal for my symptoms, anyway. Even when I took them I found that allergies disrupted my sleep, my energy, and my mood for months at a time.

Given that my allergies had been with me for decades, I never really expected them to go away. Maybe that's why I was so skeptical when I met Dr. Han and he told me about the product he was developing.

As someone who taught science for 40 years at the high school and college level I had a hard time believing that his solution, which sounded like a bunch of nice-tasting lollipops, would do much good. After all, I'd been to specialists and gotten shots. If the strongest medicines couldn't cure me, then what was a little candy *really* going to do? I almost wondered whether eating them would cause some weird side effects like having my hair fall out.

Eventually, though, I was persuaded to give them a try. After all, Dr. Han seemed to know his science and I really did want to believe there was a solution to my allergy problems.

At first, I did a cycle of three or four AllerPops and then forgot about them. In a few days I noticed a mild reduction in my allergy symptoms. I chalked it up to coincidence but also resolved to do another cycle after a few days. I never even got through the first box. My breathing got progressively better and better. By my third cycle of pops my breathing was easy. I wasn't itchy or having trouble sleeping. It was like my allergies just got up in the night and moved out.

People talk about things being "unbelievable," but for me the experience was literally beyond my level of acceptance. I assumed I had missed something. I just knew the changes couldn't have come from something as simple as eating a few lollipops. I went online to check pollen counts and found that between the ragweed, juniper pollen, and high wind speeds in the area I should have been suffering worse than ever before. And yet somehow I wasn't.

It was at this point that I started giving AllerPops to my friends. I explained to them the night-and-day changes I'd been through, and then told them to follow the instructions closely. When my results were duplicated in their experiences, I finally started to accept that the product might actually work *even better than advertised*. How rare is that?

Obviously, I'm happy to recommend AllerPops to anyone suffering with allergies. What really amazes me, though, is that they don't just work on a specific allergen like pollen. For me, the ultimate test came when I decided to babysit a friend's cat. I have always loved the little creature to death, even though holding him meant the hassle of itchy skin and watery eyes. This time there was no allergic reaction. I was able to play with him allergy-free for the first time ever.

These days, I don't worry about blooming pollen or neighborhood pets. I sleep better and don't have to spend half of my salary on tissues. It's the kind of transformation I wouldn't have thought was possible, and I'm so grateful to Dr. Han for his creation.

Shannon
Los Alamos, New Mexico

...

"Everything Changed for Us"

I never knew much about allergies or understood how they could affect someone's quality of life so dramatically. That changed when I met my wife. When pollen season would come around she would suffer through symptoms that were bad enough to require multiple shots. I felt bad that she had to deal with watery eyes and congestion, but figured it was just part of life.

My awareness of allergies intensified when my son was born. From his earliest days it seemed like he was allergic to *everything* – including pollen, mold, and animals. His reactions were even more severe than my wife's. Once he started wheezing and coughing he wouldn't always be able to catch his breath. In fact, things got so bad at a couple of points that we had to take him to the emergency room. Those were scary times.

We took him to see doctors, of course, but the best they could do was give him the same kinds of shots my wife had been taking. These measures helped, but they certainly didn't eliminate the problem. Things got even tougher when my younger daughter was born. It didn't take long to see signs she would be affected by seasonal allergies, as well.

By the summer of 2020 we were struggling. It should have been a beautiful part of the year with so many kinds of trees and flowers in full bloom. However, my wife and children were so congested they couldn't enjoy the long days. I can remember one five- or six-week stretch where we barely let the kids out of the house at all. When they did play outside, for an hour or two, we made them wear goggles. It felt extreme but their symptoms were getting worse and, having already been to the hospital for my son's coughing and lack of air, my wife and I didn't want to risk bigger problems.

The turning point came when I found myself scrolling through online investment opportunities one night. I was looking through dozens of listings and none had caught my eye until I came across the description for AllerPops. The ideas Dr. Han described were certainly intriguing, but I wanted to find out if his product had real value before investing my money. So, I ordered a couple of boxes for my family and decided to wait for the results.

My wife is a very detail-oriented person. She was also tired of struggling with allergies year after year. That made her the perfect test case: she followed the instructions that came with the pops very precisely. After she noticed her symptoms subsiding we decided to share them with our children, as well.

I don't want to sound too dramatic, but everything has changed for us since then. My wife and son haven't had any issues. My daughter is completely allergy-free. It's like she never had any symptoms in the first place. We keep some allergy medicine around as a last resort, but we haven't needed it. We simply use more pops when pollen is high or a few sniffles return. We have even been able to adopt a dog.

It would be hard to say what it means to us to allow our children to live normal lives without constantly worrying about pollen conditions... or worse, dreading the next trip to the hospital. This has been the second year in a row we've kept a continuous supply of AllerPops around the house. I would recommend them to anyone who suffers from allergies without hesitation.

Dr. Han's product has been literally life-changing for my family. I hope my story will help others find relief for themselves and their loved ones, too.

Lance
Northern Virginia

...

*You can read more firsthand accounts from AllerPops customers
at allerpops.com.*

10

FOOD ALLERGY EXPERIMENTS AND OBSERVATIONS

P lease recognize that this chapter (like the rest of this book) represents my personal opinions and research. It is not meant as medical advice, and you should never make major changes to your diet or lifestyle without consulting a physician and/or nutritionist. I want to provide my own ideas and perspectives, but your health must be your own responsibility.

My strongest allergic reactions have always revolved around sneezing, watery eyes, and a congested nasal passage. So, that's where I devoted most of my research. It's also why I developed a product that focuses on the nose and mouth. However, years of allergy study taught me that the majority of good bacteria in a human body lives in the gut. As I got further into my research I started to wonder whether the same principles would play out in the digestive tract.

In other words, was there anything I could apply about what I'd learned that would be useful in understanding food allergies?

As with my previous endeavors, this wasn't an academic question. I suspected I was dealing with some food allergy issues myself. I just didn't know what they were, or how I might be able to deal with them. To help you understand why, let me take you back once more to an entirely different time in my life.

My Tortured Love of Pasta and Noodles

One of the deep ironies associated with allergies is that we can often be irritated by the things we love most. I've talked to avid hikers who had to avoid the outdoors because of pollen. I've known pet owners who were crazy for their cats and dogs but were driven to sneezing fits when they come near. And I don't doubt there are millions of others, like me, who have allergies to the foods they crave most.

My own love of pasta and noodles goes all the way back to my childhood. Being born and raised in the Shandong province of China meant that I wasn't often exposed to these foods as a child. For those who don't know, the Yangtze River divides the country into northern and southern regions. In the south there is plenty of moisture, so grains and rice grow quite readily. But in the north, it's much harder to maintain these crops. So even though wheat was one of the main crops in Shandong, yield was always very poor.

This shortage of wheat was exacerbated even further by government policies. In the 1950s and '60s the official state planners made a number of errors, leading to low crop yields and poor harvests. There just wasn't enough to go around. Not much wheat was grown in my area, and what little my village did produce went to the government as a tax.

The staple of our everyday diet was a kind of savory pancake made from corn and dried sweet potatoes. To make them, the kids in the village would have to slice out thin pieces of sweet potato and then dry them out for storage. Next, women in the village (usually my mother and aunts) made the pancakes by rolling a dough made with corn and sweet potato flours on hot iron discs. Each one was about two feet in diameter. The resulting pancake was very thin, half dried, and lasted for a couple of weeks at ambient temperature. It was a durable kind of food, but it hardly tasted of anything at all. Looking back, that wasn't the worst thing, considering the taste that *was* present closely resembled rubber. It certainly wasn't enjoyable, but in a country that regularly experienced famine, we were happy to eat anything at all.

There were breaks to this dull culinary routine, though. From time to time – perhaps during spring festival, a visit from a far-away relative, or some other special occasion – my grandma would take out the rare ingredients needed for her daughters-in-law to make more delicious food. Those materials could be used to make noodles, dumplings, or even buns. The resulting treats were more valuable to us than gold. Things like cookies and fried dough twists had to be hung in high places to keep them away from mice, greedy cats, or their most cunning natural predators, the fourteen hungry kids who could access the kitchen. It was always so hard to be patient and wait for a big dinner.

I used to *love* these meals. It still makes my mouth water to think about them now. I can vividly picture my mother hand rolling the noodles, pouring egg soup over them, and then letting them cool. When she was finished, and when everyone had *finally* sat for dinner, I could enjoy a treat.

To put this story into context I should admit that my mother probably wasn't such a skilled cook. In fact, I'm sure I could buy better noodles and buns any time I want them now. But the noodles came around so infrequently that every one of those dinners felt special. It's always easier to want what you can't have.

I became even more attached to these treats when we moved away from our small village for my father's new job. The buns they served in his workplace were even better than the ones I had gotten at home. I later learned that it was because my mother had used flour made from multiple grains due to the wheat shortage. The work cafeteria wasn't so restricted. Sometimes I would arrive late, after the rest of the food was gone, and sprinkle several steamed buns with salt for my dinner. It was fantastic.

My love affair with wheat continued while I was studying at Suzhou Medical College. We only got noodles once a week there, and usually they had been cooked for far too long. As a result they disintegrated, becoming less of a noodle soup and more of a featureless paste. Accordingly, these were named *ruined noodles* or *overcooked paste noodles*. It was the sort of dish that might have gotten a daughter-in-law scolded and returned to her parents' home. Still, after three years I learned to love them. They might not have been prepared to perfection, but I found them to be delicious.

Later, when I graduated, I was able to get even more flavorful noodles in Fudan. This was closer to Shanghai, and the food improved as you gravitated towards the big city. Their noodles weren't ruined. Instead, they were boiled in clear broth and topped with pork steaks that had been hammered into flour, deep-fried, and finished with braising. These dishes were even better than the ones I had already tried.

All of these tastes and memories I brought with me when I came to New Mexico in 1996. I was new to the area, had no wife, and could barely communicate. I needed to learn to cook for myself. Not surprisingly I quickly developed a noodle soup recipe that I couldn't get enough of. I loved it so much I can still remember it by heart. It featured four eggs, two sausages in white oil, 400 grams of cabbage, two green onions, and 800 grams of dried noodles.

It would be hard to overstate how much I enjoyed eating that dish. I once had my family visit China for a month. While they were gone I cooked a pot of noodles every morning and ate it for all three meals. By the time they came back home I had gained a dozen pounds. But so what? I was in heaven eating my favorite food all month long.

If you've read this far into the book you can probably see where things are headed. My noodle-filled dream couldn't last forever.

It was around 2014 that my relationship with noodles started to become abusive. I didn't understand what was happening at the time, but when I look back I believe I was experiencing the first symptoms of an autoimmune sensitivity to wheat.

During this period I was already struggling with a congested nose and sleepless nights. A doctor diagnosed me as having autoimmune dermatitis – or more specifically, psoriasis on my face. The initial reaction, as usual, was to identify the problem as a "skin issue." I was prescribed a hormone ointment, which could only decrease the itching and redness for a few days at a time.

Eventually, I did find *some* relief. It seemed like a coincidence at the time, but my psoriasis lessened when I found my breakthrough with AllerPops. Not long after that, some of my first customers told the same story. In addition to easier breathing, better sleep, and clear eyes, buyers were reporting fewer problems with digestion and itchy skin. I began to suspect that there was some link between the good bacteria I was introducing into my throat and the apparent improvement in gastrointestinal health.

I might have pursued this link more intentionally if the disappearance of my symptoms had been permanent or consistent. Instead, I found that my skin issues were progressing further. In fact, there was space behind my ear that had become itchy, red, and swollen. On the whole, my problem seemed to be getting worse.

The only sustained improvement came when I had decided to study the effects of food on coliforms (a type of bacteria) and immunity. For a week I ate nothing but beef and cranberry juice. My dermatitis nearly disappeared. Given what I knew of traditional microbiome science, which suggested an increased need for fiber rather than protein, I couldn't make sense of the results. I couldn't explain what was happening. So, I once again put my findings to the side and turned back to research that tied more directly to the nose and throat.

Ultimately, my personal breakthrough with food allergies didn't come from a microscope, textbook, or even a detailed statistical analysis. Instead, it arrived in the form of a YouTube video.

I happened to be online watching an interview with Jordan Peterson, a popular author and professor. In the particular clip I saw he was talking about his daughter, who suffers from various autoimmune diseases that include allergies to many popular foods. Through trial and error he found that eating beef, and *only* beef, solved all her problems.

Further exploration on YouTube led me to a video by Ben Warren. He observed that wheat allergies are the most common among those traced back to food. These two data points were enough for me to design an experiment for myself. I stopped eating any foods with wheat flour for a week and made notes about the results. In less than seven days I noticed my dermatitis was subsiding! The irritation on the skin behind my ear was barely noticeable. But, if I went back to eating flour, the itchy skin would come back with a vengeance.

Further notetaking revealed that it wasn't only wheat flour that could cause issues. Eating apples could also wake that patch of irritated skin. And once it started, it could last anywhere from ten hours to a whole day.

With these observations in place, I started to develop some new theories and ideas.

·   ·   ·

THE INTERACTION BETWEEN FOODS, Allergy Symptoms, and Our Immune Systems

I can't say exactly when I started to be allergic to flour. Knowing what I know now, I think it was sometime after I began experiencing seasonal allergies in 2014. Everything that I've learned about allergies, the hygiene hypothesis, and the way our immune systems interface with the external world supports this idea.

My theory is not that flour and apples are stimulating the immune system in my mouth and esophagus. I believe the irritation is taking place in my small intestine. After my overactive immune system is activated by the "pathogens" of these foods, it causes or worsens problems in other parts of the body. This would explain, for instance, why I stopped eating all forms of noodles and pasta the year I found that my allergic rhinitis nearly disappeared in the spring. It makes sense that changing my eating, while using AllerPops, would stop me from experiencing those food allergies.

There isn't any reason to think that food allergies are much different to the body than nasal and throat allergies. They represent the same problem, an autoimmune response triggered by a lack of good bacteria. It's simply the same issue presenting with a different set of symptoms. The attached chart summarizes (in broad strokes) the different ways the irritation can show itself.

Immune System	Probiotics	Healthy balance	Prebiotics	Activators	Pacifiers
Oral -stomach	Streptococcus/Veillonella. Bacteria can grow in the mouth especially on the tongue, on the teeth, and in the pocket between teeth and gums.	A moderate growth of oral microbiota including the probiotics is necessary for the health of the immune system and teeth and gums.	Saliva	Pathogens, allergens, excessive oral hygiene, some kind of food that suppress oral bacteria	AllerPops
Small intestine	Small intestine starts with almost no bacteria to a limited bacterial growth at the end of the ileum, not enough to produce sufficient immune pacifying metabolites.	Traditionally: metabolites from saliva may play a significant role to calm down the immune system Modern: likely not enough for many people	NA	Pathogens, allergens, fermented food	Metabolite supplements such as short-chain fatty acids for people with allergies or autoimmune issues
Large Intestine	Fiber-degrading bacteria	Enough fiber-degrading bacteria overcomes the stimulation effect of the whole microbiota.	Food with fibers	Pathogens, allergens, unabsorbed food nutrients, colon cleanse	Indigestible food fibers
Airway	Streptococcus/ Veillonella, reseeded with droplet from mouth when eating, breathing and talking	Enough metabolites produced to calm down the local immune cells	Mucus	Pathogens, allergens	AllerPops

You can find detailed descriptions of the human immune system online, or in academic books. In this chapter I only want to offer two main points about its relationship to microbiota. First, our immune system is strategically located in places interfacing the outside world, where most pathogen attacks happen. These include the digestive tracts (70%), airway (20%), and skin (5%). Many bacteria and other microbes that do not usually cause disease live in these places.

To maintain peaceful relationships with our immune system, the key members of the microbiotas use probiotics that can send signals to our cells that cease the immune reaction (i.e., attack) that would otherwise result. Different probiotics feed on corresponding prebiotics (food) available naturally at the place they occupy. These good bacteria will of course go away (mostly) when infection occurs so that the immune system can fight the pathogen freely.

Second, immune responses are generally systemic. That means immune system actions in one part of the body may also help fight infection in a different location. It could also worsen allergies (as an autoimmune reaction) in another place. For example, we are evolved to have less appetite even when an infection, especially one with fever, is not in the digestive tracts. While there are many other explanations, one reason may be that the body wants to starve the "good" bacteria in the gut to release the immune power in that region to fight the problem elsewhere. Therefore, "starving a fever" is likely accomplished through starving the gut bacteria that would normally live there.

When you have allergies, the immune system – from the mouth to the small intestine – is overactive and searching for threats. Mine has always been watching out for what I eat. It has been pondering, researching, and experimenting with new defenses until finally, one day, it activated a potent antibody against flour and apples. With that, a lifetime love was extinguished. I can no longer enjoy these foods without a cost.

However, that doesn't mean that I have to say goodbye to these foods forever. It could be that further study will lead myself, a colleague, or some other researcher looking for a cure for allergies to finally nail down a treatment. Maybe there is an *AllerBiscuit* that can be developed. Imagine the relief that would bring to so many millions who are unable to eat their favorite foods... or are currently suffering from a food allergy without even being aware of it.

For the time being I can only report on my own theories and findings. If you have a food allergy, or suspect you are being affected by one, I would encourage you to speak to your doctor and do some research online. You may find that making a few small changes to your lifestyle and diet could help with skin issues, irritated bowels, or even mental symptoms like low energy or a lack of concentration.

It's been a long time since I had noodles with my family. I've had to say goodbye to the Sanxian dumplings and shallot sesame oil pancakes I love so much, at least for now. I am very much looking forward to the day when I can eat them again, but it hasn't arrived yet. As an experienced time traveler, at least I can hold hope for the future!

11

THE FUTURE OF THE HYGIENE HYPOTHESIS

I f you have followed me this far into the book, then you know all about me, my story, and the product I've created. You know why I'm not just an entrepreneur, but someone who is on a mission to bring relief to millions.

With all of that out of the way, it was tempting to simply end the book with some kind words and success stories from AllerPops customers. But then I remembered this book isn't really about me. In a certain sense it isn't even about my company.

Some of you may be reading about the hygiene hypothesis for the first time. Perhaps you had never heard of prebiotics. You might not have even come across the idea that there are good kinds of bacteria your body needs to function correctly before these pages. And so, you might have a lot of questions. After all, we are *all* scientists and time travelers at heart – the way we adapt to new situations and information is by learning and exploring.

Rather than simply leaving you with my story, I wanted to pull you up to my scientific water tower and give you a glimpse of what might be coming in our future. Certainly, I recommend you look at other reading materials on the subject, like the best-seller *An Epidemic of Absence*. But if you're wondering what sort of current implications come from my theory, want to know about future research possibilities, or are just curious about the future of my company, then read on.

The Human Biome Is a Whole New World

One of the best things about our world, and our lives, is that there is always something new to discover. Once upon a time, explorers set off into the ocean and learned there were unknown continents and populations waiting to be found. After those were mapped, we started exploring the depths of the ocean, and the vast, endless reaches of space.

Those explorations will continue for a long, long time. They may never end. But the newest frontier in the world of science isn't far away – it's *within*.

You may have noticed, in my chapter on the hygiene hypothesis, that the studies I referenced were all fairly recent. We've been learning about things like gravity and anatomy for centuries, but the microbiome that exists within the human body is a relatively new discovery. Although we have known about bacteria for decades, we are only beginning to scratch the surface when it comes to understanding how these organisms interact with us and each other.

Our immune systems serve as border guards to the bacteria living with us. Proper communication needs to be established at every boundary that lies between our body and the outside world of microbes. The skin, airways, and reproductive or digestive tracts are all vulnerable places. These are also the areas where our immune systems do most of their work.

We don't yet know how all the microbial pieces fit together. Some early studies suggest that there could be relationships between certain bacterial strains and digestion. Others point to the prevalence of skin issues and autoimmune disorders. There are even biologists who think that psychological conditions like depression might be affected by the type and amount of bacteria found within your body.

These relationships still need to be uncovered and explored, of course, and it's likely that many of them will be complex. It took me years of work to understand that there were two different bacterial groups with dozens of species related to simple allergy symptoms. Who knows what might be revealed in the decades to come?

The only thing we can be certain of is that medical science will likely change and evolve significantly in our lifetimes. Now that we've looked inward we are discovering a whole new ecosystem to be treated and understood.

IMAGINING New Treatments for Disease

One of the things that make prebiotics and probiotics such an interesting field of study is that they aren't really *treatments* as much as they are *enablers*. By that I mean they give the body the tools it needs to heal itself. The more we understand about this process, the greater potential there is for new and more natural therapies, not to mention less destructive cures for common diseases or ailments.

This seems like an idea that is arriving at the right place and time in history. In some circles, so-called "traditional" or "homeopathic" treatments are gaining traction. More and more people are starting to be interested in traditional Chinese medicine, for example, both within and away from my former country. This isn't because they aren't appreciative of the benefits we all get from modern science. Instead, it's a recognition that we can go overboard in treating ourselves with potent pills and solutions.

As an example, it used to be the case that a medicine man or healer would look at a patient's tongue and evaluate the color. To many modern doctors this may come across as super-stition. However, we now know that the color of a person's tongue can indicate if they have a high temperature, or whether there is too much or too little bacteria present. It turns out that this simple observation can actually tell us something about a person's health before we inject something new into their body.

Contrast that with what happened during the Spanish flu pandemic. Just over 100 years ago (like today) a nasty respira-tory disease was sweeping the world. Doctors and nurses, trained to treat symptoms, gave patients medicines (and espe-cially aspirin, which had only just come down in price) that lowered their fevers. That might have made sick men and women feel better, at least temporarily, but it robbed the body of the weapon it needed to eradicate the virus. As a result, it is now accepted that many thousands of people died from the *treatment* for their flu rather than the illness itself.

Looking back, a bit of lukewarm water on a patient's head (to ease fever symptoms in that part of the body) would have been just as effective and much less dangerous. In studying that era we find lessons that might apply today. Most medical professionals are still trained to treat symptoms, and the majority are completely unfamiliar with the human micro-biome. As a result they may resort to tools – like overpowered antibiotics – that do more harm than good.

My hope and prediction is that these tendencies will change in the future. My expectation is that we will learn, collectively as a species, that a bit of discomfort can actually be a good thing. As an example, there is some early data suggesting that the Covid-19 pandemic, as terrible as it has been, has decreased cancer rates in certain populations. Why?

Because prolonged fevers or response to infection can stimulate strong immune defense activities that not only cure infection but also destroy cancer cells.

Looking out ten or twenty years I think it's possible that otherwise healthy people will let non-consequential viruses run their course more often. We may even have vaccines that safely induce fever and switch on our immune system within the body. That obviously runs counter to the way most illnesses are treated now, but remember we evolved in an environment that was filled with microbial threats and regular bouts of sickness. We might *need* ancient tools like fevers to help us regulate stronger defense activities that will cure/clean up our body to prevent bigger problems from coming. It could be that a little bit of sickness and discomfort today will help protect you later. There might be some wisdom in one of the world's oldest pieces of advice: what doesn't kill us makes us stronger.

Just to be clear once more, I'm not advocating for modern medicines and vaccines to go away. Nor am I telling you to forgo life-saving treatments. It's a wonderful thing that children no longer die of polio, and that you can drink water from a fountain without worrying about cholera or malaria. What I *am* hoping for is greater realization that our microbial selves are more complex than we used to know or imagine. Environments that are too dirty, and contain bad bacteria, can kill us. But living in a way that is too sterile, and too clean, can also lead to suffering.

A Product to Change the World

Having told you what I think is coming in the world of medicine, I should probably take a moment and describe what I see as the future of my company.

My biggest and most immediate hope is that in the short term, meaning the next five or ten years, AllerPops will bring relief to millions of people who can finally sleep, breathe, and enjoy the world around them. If my team and I can accomplish that one thing, then the long journey it took to reach this point in my life will have been more than worth it.

The product we have is extremely safe and effective, but that doesn't mean it can't be improved. It's not 100% effective for everyone, which means there is more testing to be done. It might be that we can change the formulation in the lab ever so slightly to make it work for more people. Or, it could be that excessive oral care has depressed the microbiome so severely in some people that we'll need to develop a new probiotic version to help them. Future research might lead us to other strains of good bacteria that reinforce the results and make relief more widely available.

This is the work that will guide me in the years to come. I know there are doctors and scientists working in labs around the world right now to overcome more severe and life-threatening conditions. But solving the problem of seasonal allergies could improve the quality of life for so many that I'm proud to have taken it up as a goal.

Looking farther onto the horizon, I can imagine a family of related products – for example, toothpastes or mouthwash mixtures – that will either encourage good bacteria growth (prebiotic) or introduce those bacteria to the mouth and throat directly (probiotic). Of course, much more research is needed in this area, and that will have to wait until AllerPops has become established in the market.

Going past that, I'm interested in finding ways to make peace with mother nature in other areas. In my own life I have learned how I could use diet and lifestyle changes to overcome hypertension, for example. I've also done some study on the topic of family relationships, having developed theories on the best ways for fathers and daughters to make peace with each other. Once you understand that everything in the world is about context, then it's easier to start making other connections.

All of that is far into the future, however. Even as I've been writing this book, stealing the odd hour to spend with my editor between other meetings, I have been pushing AllerPops farther forward. It's a nonstop process of investment, finance, marketing, and clinical trials. Sometimes it feels overwhelming, but then I remember that with each tiny step we take forward, a new person is finding relief.

And so, for the time being I will keep my focus on what's directly in front of me. There's plenty to do in my business and looking too far into the future is always an uncertain proposition, even for a time traveler like myself. No one would have ever guessed a shy and stubborn child from Hanlou would grow up to invent a life-changing product. Who knows where destiny might lead all of us next?

12

PLEASE LEAVE ME AN HONEST REVIEW

Thank you for making it all the way here. I hope you enjoyed this book and it would be great if you'd leave me a review on Amazon or Goodreads. This means a lot to me.

And, if you're looking for allergy relief, you can find more at allerpops.com.